# LITTLE BOOK OF
# TANKS

SIMON FORTY

# LITTLE BOOK OF
# TANKS

First published in the UK in 2014

© Demand Media Limited 2014

www.demand-media.co.uk

Printed and bound in Europe

ISBN 978-1-910270-21-9

# Contents

# Introduction

The war of manoeuvre that had character-ised the start of the war in 1914 on the Western Front congealed in the mud of the trenches in 1915. Defence in depth—barbed wire entanglements, carefully placed machine guns affording murderous crossfire, deep concrete and armoured bunkers to withstand artillery bombardment—guaranteed stale-mate. The need to overcome this led to a number of significant military developments, including the use of gas (the Germans used chlorine gas around Ypres in April 1915) and the birth of the tank.

Major Earnest Swinton, Lord Kitchener's official observer sent to France in 1914, sug-gested a machine-gun destroyer based on the American Holt Caterpillar tractor. His idea found favour with Winston Churchill in the Admiralty and the Landships Committee was set up. The result—code-named 'mobile water

tanks for Mesopotamia' to throw spies off the scent—was the rhomboid vehicle, nicknamed 'Mother', that graces the cap badges of the Royal Tank Regiment to this day.

The first use of tanks in combat was in 1916, by the British Army at Flers-Courcelette, part of the battle of the Somme. While the results weren't battle changing, and automotive reli-ability was a major problem, nevertheless the tanks that crossed the starting point pointed the way to a successful future.

This success was, however, a long time coming: the French used tanks for the first time on 16 April 1917, during the Nivelle offensive. It was a significant failure with half the substantial tank force destroyed by long-range artillery, and when the French heavy tank, the Saint-Chamond armed with a 75mm howitzer, first saw action on 5 May, it proved to be so badly designed that they were unable

Lincoln Machine with lengthened Bullock tracks and Creeping Grip tractor suspension, 1915.

to cross the first line of German trenches. In fact it was to be light tanks—in particular the French Renault FT 17 with its rotating turret on top of a chassis that placed the driver at the front and engine at the rear, and a proper climbing face for the tracks—that provided the template for the future.

On 20 November 1917, at Cambrai, a real penetration by tanks took place. Even after taking into account the propaganda surrounding the battle, there is no doubt that the British tanks showed what could be done and would have done better had they not been opposed by the German 54th Division, specifically trained in anti-tank tactics. In 1918, this was reinforced at Amiens on 8 August—Ludendorff's 'Black Day of the German Army'. Armoured support helped the Allies break through the German trench lines, weakening what had once been impregnable trench positions. The British Third Army with no tanks had almost no effect on the line

US recruitment poster of 1917 by August William Hurat.

while the Fourth helped break deep into German territory. There was a heavy cost, though: 72% of the Allied tanks were destroyed in the first four days. 41.4% of all British tanks had been destroyed by the 64th day. On November 5, there were only eight British tanks left.

Unsurprisingly, without any clear-cut demonstration of prowess, after the war military opinion was divided on the future of the tank—and the Depression and general poor economic climate meant there was little money to spend on research anyway. For example, in the United States, J. Walter Christie developed a revolutionary suspension chassis which was capable of high speeds, and was—in some cases—light enough to be air transportable, but disputes with the military procurement arm and a high price meant they were not produced in his homeland. The prototypes found their way to the Soviet Union, and became the basis for the BT series that would eventually be developed into the T-34.

At a time when cars themselves

This Panther, burnt out in front of Cologne Cathedral, was destroyed on 6 March 1945 by an M26 Pershing commanded by Sgt. Robert Early of US 3rd Armored Division.

were new and only just becoming plentiful, it's not surprising that most soldiers could not understand the potential of armoured vehicles. Some—such as J.F.C. Fuller, Basil Liddell Hart and Percy Hobart—foresaw a fully mechanised war and although most others did not, in Germany Heinz Guderian was one of the converted, avidly following British and French tank warfare theorists. In *Achtung Panzer!* he presented his views on the

Sherman DD tanks of the 7th Hussars, part of 7th Armoured Brigade, in the Piazzale Roma, Venice, on 30 April 1945.

future of armoured warfare: it was a blueprint for Blitzkrieg.

Lightning war came to Europe between 1939 and 1941 when German troops, spearheaded by their armoured—Panzer—divisions, closely supported by airpower, demolished the opposing European armies and conquered most of Europe. And while it is true to say that the German armoured vehicles weren't anywhere near as strong in 1940 as they would be only a year later, there were few occasions when Allied tanks were able to stop their advance. It quickly became clear that the World War II land battlefield was going to be dominated by the tank/anti-tank gun battle, policed by aircraft. It was also clear that the Germans, first with their PzKpfw IIIs and IVs then with their Panthers and Tigers and at all times with their 88mm gun were in pole position.

It took a disparate alliance to counter the Germans. The arsenal of the free world—the great industrial capability of the United States and the British Empire—and the huge capacity of the Soviets allowed the Allies to hit back. Armour was in the vanguard as Churchills, Shermans and T-34s duelled with Panzers, Panthers and Tigers in the debris of the Third Reich. The Germans may have had the better guns but the numbers were against them, and as the war went on each country gained a pro-ficiency in building battle-capable tanks. By 1945, warfare had changed and the tank—in particular what would become known as the main battle tank—dominated the battlefield.

The Cold War saw tank development reach its apogee in the MBTs of the biggest military-industrial complexes—the US Abrams, German Leopard, British Challenger, Israeli Merkava and Russian T90. But the period also saw the tank challenged: the battlefields of the Middle East were punctuated by the blackened hulks of tanks knocked out by helicopters and infantry armed with guided missiles. Many armies question the worth of these behemoths, whose enormous cost—each M1 Abrams costs $8,580,000 (€6,183,691/£5,084,988)—means few can afford the most modern equipment: to the old adage that tanks are a compromise of mobility, protection and firepower needs to be added the element of cost. Today, in a world of asymmetric warfare, expensive MBTs are as likely to be attacked by an IED as another tank.

Whatever the future, one thing is clear. The battles of the two Gulf Wars showed what happens when top-notch equipment comes up against lesser forces. The best way to beat a tank is to have a better one and the tanks in this book show the way that this has developed over the hundred years since the first tank.

# Abbreviations
## and Parts of a tank

**AA(A)** anti-aircraft (artillery)
**AEV** armoured engineer vehicle
**AFV** armoured fighting vehicle
**APC** armoured personnel carrier
**APFSDS** armour-piercing fin-stabilised discarding sabot
**ARV** armoured recovery vehicle
**ATGM** anti-tank guided missile
**Ausf** *Ausführung* (design) used to denote specific model or mark type
**AVRE** Armoured Vehicle Royal Engineers
**CVR(T)** Combat Vehicle Reconnaissance (Tracked)
**DAK** Deutsches Afrika Korps
**ERA** explosive reactive armour
**FCS** fire control system
**Flak** *Flugzeugabwehrkanone* (AA gun)

**GDLS** General Dynamics Land Systems
**GMC** gun (or H for howitzer) motor carriage
**HEAT** high explosive anti-tank
**HOT** *Haut subsonique Optiquement Téléguidé Tiré d'un Tube*, or high subsonic optical remote-guided, tube-launched anti-tank missile
**IDF** Israeli Defence Forces
**IED** improvised explosive device
**IR** infrared
**JGSDF** Japan Ground Self Defense Force
**KE** kinetic energy
**LAHAT** laser homing anti-tank

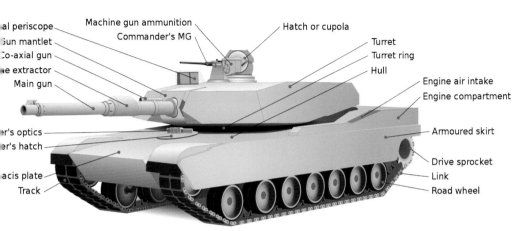

| | | | | |
|---|---|---|---|---|
| **MBT** | main battle tank | | **RTR** | Royal Tank Regiment |
| **MG** | machine gun | | **RWS** | remotely controlled weapons station |
| **Mk** | mark | | | |
| **MoD** | Ministry of Defence | | **Sd Kfz** | *Sonderkraftfahrzeug* (special purpose vehicle) the ordnance inventory designation for German WWII military vehicles |
| **NBC** | nuclear, biological, chemical | | | |
| **pdr** | pounder | | | |
| **PIAT** | Projectile Infantry Anti-Tank; WWII British anti-tank weapon | | | |
| | | | **SEP** | System Enhancement Package |
| **PzKpfw** | *Panzerkampfwagen:* Armoured battle vehicle = tank | | **SPAAG** | self-propelled AA gun |
| **RMG** | ranging machine gun | | **StuG** | *Sturmgeschütz* (assault gun) |
| **ROF** | Royal Ordnance Factory | | **TUSK** | tank urban survival kit |
| **ROK** | Republic of Korea | | **WL** | white light |
| **RPG** | rocket-propelled grenade | | **WWI/II** | World War I or II |

# No I Lincoln Machine ('Little Willie')

## Prototype | United Kingdom | 1915

**E**rnest Swinton, the official British war correspondent on the Western Front, was instrumental in starting tank development after he saw a Holt's tractor towing a gun. In early 1915 the Landships Committee was set up to examine armoured vehicles. By autumn 1915 Little Willie had been devised.

The first tank ever built, it was a prototype produced to meet a War Office requirement— to cross a 4ft wide trench and mount a 2f vertical step. Designed by Lt. Gordon Wilson and agricultural engineer William Tritton of Lincoln-based William Foster & Co, Little Willie was originally planned to have a centrally mounted turret with a 2pdr gun, but it had a problematic gestation. The British designed Bullock tracks, which had been manufactured commercially in America, never gripped as well as necessary and when the War Office revised its tests, Little Willie had to be rebuilt to cross a 5ft trench and climb a 4.5ft step. It had a rectangular hull and sepa

---

### SPECIFICATION

**Crew: 4–6**
**Entered service: 1915 (prototype)**
**Weight: 18.290kg (18 tons)**
**Dimensions:**
**Length: 5.53m (18ft 2in)**
**Height: 3.05m (10ft 2in)**
**Width: 2.8m (9ft 4in)**
**Armour: 12mm (0.5in)**

**Engine: Daimler 6-cylinder petrol developing 105hp with a top speed of 3.2kph (2mph)**
**Range: Not tested**
**Armament:**
**Main: (Projected) Vickers 2-pounder gun**
**Secondary: (Projected) Various suggestions of machine guns**

The first tank: 'Little Willie' was built in 1915.

rate tail wheels, which were towed behind to help with steering and improve cross-country performance; they would be retained in early production versions. By early December 1915 Little Willie had served its purpose. The first operational tank, the Mark I, would incorporate many of the design features tested on Little Willie. Preserved, it can be seen at the Tank Museum in Bovington, Dorset.

# Mark I ('Mother')

## Heavy Tank | United Kingdom | 1916

The problems encountered during the construction of Little Willie—particularly those relating to the tracks—were solved with 'Mother', this name sticking where previous terms, including Centipede, had not. A rhomboidal shape allowed longer track length, which considerably improved cross-country performance and enabled 'Mother' to pass the War Office tests, even after the requirements had changed to crossing an 8ft trench. Weapons were housed in side-mounted sponsons to keep the centre of gravity low when the vehicle mounted trench parapets.

The Landships Committee had became the Tank Supply Committee and although opinions on the tank's usefulness were mixed (Secretary of State for War Field Marshal Kitchener was unimpressed), in February 1916 100 Mk Is were ordered under the direction of the Minister of Munitions, David Lloyd George. The end product was a lumbering behemoth, whose internal space was noisy, cramped and almost unbearable to fight in. The armour

| SPECIFICATION | |
|---|---|
| Crew: **8** | Engine: **Daimler 6-cylinder petrol developing 150hp with a top speed of 5.95kph (3.7mph)** |
| Entered service: **1916** | |
| Weight: **28,450kg (28 tons)** | |
| Dimensions: | Range: **35.4km (22 miles)** |
| Length: **9.9m (32ft 6in)** | Armament: |
| Height: **2.41m (7ft 11in)** | Main: **2 x 6pdr guns** |
| Width: **4.19m (13ft 9in)** | Secondary: **1 x 0.303in Hotchkiss MG** |
| Armour: **10mm (under 0.5in)** | |

Mark I series tank and crewman, 1916. The chicken wire is probably used to keep grenades away from the hull. The armour of the early models wasn't very thick.

proved initially effective against small-arms fire but the Germans quickly developed more penetrative weapons forcing the crew to wear cumbersome masks to protect themselves against spall. Communications inside the tank were difficult and virtually impossible with the outside world save by pigeon. The initial order was increased to 150 and was fulfilled by Fosters (25) and the Birmingham-based Metropolitan Amalgamated Railway Carriage and Wagon Company Ltd. Shortage of 6pdr guns led to half being equipped with machine guns—Ernest Swinton called these 'Females', the gun tanks being 'Males'.

The Mk I saw action for the first time during the Battle of the Somme in 1916. All the tanks available at the time—49—were thrown into action at Flers-Courcelette on 15 September 1916. Only 15 tanks of C and D Companies Heavy Section Machine Gun Corps managed to advance past the front line—mechanical problems dogged the early vehicles—but their undoubted value led to the famous report, 'A tank is walking down the High Street of Flers with the British Army cheering behind.'

# Mark IV/Mark V

## Heavy Tank | United Kingdom | 1917

Unsurprisingly, the technology of the tank developed quickly under the combat conditions of World War I. The Mk IV, introduced in late 1917, had changed considerably from the Mk I: the steering wheels, so necessarily for Little Willie, had proved ineffective and had gone; the long barrel of the 6pdr had been shortened; armour had been improved to defeat the German anti-tank rifles; the fuel tank had been placed for safety in an external container; and the sponsons could be swung inward to help rail transportation. Perhaps most important of all, thought had been given to the problem of bogging down in the mud of the trenches and the myriad shell holes. The answer was a set of rails on the roof of the tank that could carry a fascine to fill a trench or an unditching beam. The beam could be attached to the tracks and pulled under the tank to assist adhesion and allow the tracks to get some purchase.

The most numerous British tank of the war—over 1,000 Mk IVs were built, more females than males—it first saw

| SPECIFICATION | |
|---|---|
| Variant: **Mk IV** | Armour: **12mm (0.50in) max** |
| Crew: **8** | Engine: **Daimler 6-cylinder petrol** |
| Entered service: **1917** | **developing 100hp with a top speed** |
| Weight: **28,450kg (28 tons)** | **of 6kph (under 4mph)** |
| Dimensions: | Range: **40km (25 miles)** |
| Length: **8.03m (26ft 4in)** | Armament: |
| Height: **2.49m (8ft 2in)** | Main: **2 x 6pdr gun** |
| Width: **3.91m (12ft 10in)** | Secondary: **4 x 0.303in Lewis MGs** |

action at Messines in June 1917. However, it was the use of tanks, most of them Mk IVs, at Cambrai on 20 November 1917 that would prove to the world that it had become a significant weapon of war. 450 tanks—mainly Mk IVs—penetrated further in one day than the Passchendaele offensive had managed in five months. 20 November—Cambrai Day—is still honoured by the Royal Tank Regiment.

The Mk V was another step forward. It had a four-speed epicyclic gearbox that replaced the change-speed gearing of earlier models thus dispensing with the need for a secondary gearsman. There were other improvements: improved observation and ventilation; an increase in range afforded by a better engine and improved fuel capacity; and better crew escape hatches in the roof.

The Mk V first saw action at Hamel on 4 July 1918 and is also noteworthy for its use by US 301st Heavy Tank Battalion particularly against the Hindenburg Line at the battles of St Quentin Canal and the Selle in October

Mark V 'female' during the battle of Amiens in August 1918: note the smaller sponsons.

1918. The Mk V also saw a number of interesting further developments: the modification of a number to become 'hermaphrodites' with one sponson mounting a 'male' 6pdr and the other a 'female' machine gun; the addition of Tritton's so-called 'tadpole tail' which saw the Mk V* lengthened by 6ft to improve its trench-crossing ability (nearly 600 of these were built by the Armistice); and the Mk V** which addressed the problems to steering this extra length caused.

# Renault FT 17

## Light Tank | France | 1917

One of the most successful of the early tank designs, the *Char Mitrailleuse* (machine gun tank) FT 17 was a lightweight tank that proved surprisingly long-lived: the French Army still had 1,560 in service when the Germans invaded in 1940. The first tank to have a fully traversing turret, containing either a single Hotchkiss 8mm machine gun or a Puteaux 37mm cannon—the turret was designed to be moulded, but production difficulties led to a riveted eight-sided turret instead. After a slow manufacturing start from March 1917, 2,613 were built in 1918 and eventually production ceased after 3,694 had been built. Pushed on by the head of the French tank corps, Brigadier General Jean-Baptiste Eugène Estienne, the French took 3,177 and the Americans 514. The British also used them, mainly for command and liaison work.

The FT 17 first saw combat at Retz in May 1918 as part of Tenth Army's attempt to slow the German Spring Offensive. As numbers reached the battlefield it became increasingly influential, although 746 were lost to enemy action. After the

### SPECIFICATION

Crew: **2**
Entered service: **1917**
Weight: **6,604kg (6.5 tons)**
Dimensions:
Length: **4.09m (13ft 6in)**
Height: **2.13m (7ft)**
Width: **1.7m (5ft 7in)**

Armour: **22mm (0.9in)**
Engine: **Renault 4-cylinder petrol developing 35hp with a top speed of 7.7kph (4.8mph)**
Range: **35km (22 miles)**
Armament: **1 x 8mm Hotchkiss MG**

950 FT 17s were built in the United States as the M1917.

war it was much copied and a number of countries used the FT 17 as the basis for their own light tank designs, most notably the Russian KS, the Italian Fiat 3000 and the American Six-ton tank, and the Japanese Types 92 and 94 were also influenced by FT 17 trials.

# A7V Sturmpanzerwagen

## Heavy Tank | Germany | 1917

**T**he advent of British tanks in 1916 galvanised the other combatants in World War I and soon other armoured vehicles were in production. The Germans reacted quite slowly but eventually designed and built the ungainly A7V—the designation alluding to *Allgemeines Kriegsdepartement, 7. Verkehrswesen Abteilung* (General War Department, 7th Section Traffic)—*Sturmpanzerwagen* (assault armoured vehicle). Big and boxlike, it was speedy on firm ground but poor over rough or muddy terrain. 100 were ordered but fewer than 25 came into service. The large 18-man crew included 12 machine gunners. The main nose-mounted armament was a 57mm Sokol gun—the same type that was used on captured British tanks—*Beute Panzerwagen*. Cross-country performance was poor, but its road speed was high although it was mechanically unreliable.

The A7V took part in the first tank v tank battle on 24 April 1918: when *Nixe* and two other A7Vs came upon two (Female) and one (Male) British Mark

## SPECIFICATION

| | |
|---|---|
| Crew: **18** | Engine: **2 x Daimler-Benz 4-cylinder petrol developing 100hp with a top speed of 15kph (9mph)** |
| Entered service: **1917** | |
| Weight: **30,480kg (30 tons)** | |
| Dimensions: | Range: **70km (44 miles)** |
| Length: **8m (26ft 3in)** | Armament: |
| Height: **3.4m (11ft 2in)** | Main: **1 x 5.7mm gun** |
| Width: **3.2m (10ft 6in)** | Secondary: **6 x 7.92mm Maxim-Spandau 08/15 MGs** |
| Armour: **30mm (1.2in)** | |

An A7V in action, June 1918.

IV heavy tanks near Villers-Bretonneux. *Nixe's* armour-piercing machine gun fire tore holes in the British Females who were forced to withdraw, but accurate fire from 2Lt Frank Mitchell's Male's 6pdr—he hit the A7V three times—forced it to take evasive action, and in doing so 2Lt Wilhelm Biltz's tank ran down a steep bank and overturned. Mitchell was able to see off the other two A7Vs and British Whippets successfully drove off the accompanying German infantry, but the British then came under artillery fire and Mitchell's Mk IV was abandoned after losing a track.

Earlier in the day, another A7V—*Mephisto*—had been abandoned after falling onto its side. It was taken by Australian troops during a counter-attack a few days later and today can be seen in the Queensland Museum in Brisbane.

# BT series

## Medium Tank | USSR | 1932

The BT series of tanks were produced in large numbers in the 1930s, the initials BT short for the Russian words for 'high speed' or 'fast tank'. They were known as cavalry tanks and were used in a similar ways to cavalry units—for fast charges to swamp enemy lines or positions. They were based on the M1931 design by J. Walter Christie for a convertible AFV that had road wheels as well as tracks. Two of Christie's prototypes were smuggled to Russia as 'agricultural tractors' and the Russians produced their own version in late 1931, three BT-2 prototypes followed by full production in 1932. It was armed with a 37mm main gun and a machine gun but owing to a shortage of heavy guns they were often seen mounting three machine guns instead.

The next—and main production—version was the BT-5, armed with an updated 45mm main gun. In 1935 the BT-7 appeared, then BT-7M with a diesel engine. This had a top speed of 40mph and a 76.2mm main gun.

In just over a decade of

| SPECIFICATION | |
|---|---|
| Variant: **BT-5** | Armour: **6–13mm (0.23-0.5in)** |
| Crew: **3** | Engine: **Model M-5 petrol developing 400hp with a top speed of 72kph (45mph)** |
| Entered service: **1933** | |
| Weight: **11,500kg (12.7 tons)** | |
| Dimensions: | Range: **200 km (120 miles)** |
| Length: **5.58 m (18ft 4in)** | Armament: |
| Width: **2.23m (7ft 4in)** | Main: **1 x 45mm Model 32 gun** |
| Height: **2.25m (7ft 5in)** | Secondary: **1 x 7.62mm (0.3in) DT MG** |

The BT-7 entered service in 1936. It had an improved conical turret and a 45mm main gun.

manufacture many BT variants were produced, including an artillery support vehicle armed with a 76.2mm howitzer, a 420mm rocket launcher, a flamethrower and an amphibious variant along with the new turrets to carry these weapon systems and increases in the thickness of the armour.

The final research and development of the BT series would be the precursor and parent of the Soviet's finest tank of WWII, the T-34.

# Sd Kfz 101 PzKpfw I

## Light Tank | Germany | 1934

When one thinks of Blitzkrieg it's easy to think that the Germans swept through Europe behind deadly ranks of heavy tanks. Nothing could be further from the truth: the majority of the armoured vehicles used between 1939 and 1941 were PzKpfw I and IIs. Restricted by the Treaty of Versailles from building tanks, during the 1920s and 1930s various vehicles were surreptitiously designed and tested—some of them at a training centre at Kazan in the USSR. Two important champions of armoured warfare were involved the Inspector of Motorised Troops, General Lutz, and his chief of staff, Heinz Guderian then a lieutenant-colonel. They needed a training tank and so the *Heereswaffenamt* (Army Weapons Branch) invited five firms to tender for a 5-ton light tank armed with two machine guns in a traversable turret. The result was the '*Landwirtschaftlicher Schlepper*' (agricultural tractor) whose design was completed in December 1933.

Production of what became the Ausf A stated in July 1934 and

---

## SPECIFICATION

| | |
|---|---|
| **Variant: Ausf B** | **Armour: 13mm (0.5in)** |
| **Crew: 2** | **Engine: Maybach NL38TR 6-cylinder** |
| **Entered service: 1935** | **petrol developing 100hp with a top** |
| **Weight: 5,893kg (5.8 tons)** | **speed of 40kph (25mph)** |
| **Dimensions:** | **Range: 170km (105 miles)** |
| **Length: 4.42m (14ft 6in)** | **Armament:** |
| **Height: 1.72m (5ft 8in)** | **Main: 2 x 7.92mm MG13s** |
| **Width: 2.06m (6ft 9in)** | |

PzKpfw I Ausf A. Note the five road wheels and three return rollers. The Ausf B had four return rollers.

around 500 were built. As might be expected the first German tank to go into mass production had problems—mainly the suspension, engine overheating and under-protection from very thin armour. The Ausf A was withdrawn from active service in 1941. The Ausf B had a longer chassis and a more powerful engine. It entered service in 1935 and was also phased out in 1941. Both Ausf A and B were deployed during the Spanish Civil War and the Anschluss and these rehearsals for Blitzrieg showed up a number of places for improvement, particularly to the

repair and recovery services.

Other PzKpfw I variants were built. The Ausf C, was designed as a fast recce vehicle, but the order didn't see completion until 1942 and most of the vehicles ended up being used for training. The Ausf D was a projected heavier infantry tank version: the prototype ran in June 1940 before the project was abandoned. Finally, there was the *Kleiner Panzerbefehlswagen* (Sd Kfz 265)—small command vehicle. This was used in the Polish and Western Blitzkrieg operations.

# Sd Kfz 121 PzKpfw II

## Light Tank | Germany | 1935

**W**ith the PzKpfw III and IV still in gestation, another light training tank was built: the PzKpfw II, which was planned to be better armoured and armed than its predecessor, but still fall below 10 tons. It proved to be a durable machine and saw considerable service from its issue in 1935. There were three main models, the Ausf A, B and C. The Ausf A had no cupola and the commander had to make do with a periscope. The Ausf B saw improvements to armour and vision devices and the addition of a commander's cupola. The Ausf C had thicker armour, which increased the weight and formed the basis for a variety of different models: the Ausf D and E had Christie-style suspension that increased road speed but gave poor cross-country performance. These were soon taken out of service and 95 were converted to become flamethrowers, others became SP guns. Further variants—the Ausf F, G and J—were uparmoured versions built 1940–41. The Ausf L (Sd Kfz 123) *Luchs* (Lynx) was built for the reconnaissance role

### SPECIFICATION

| | |
|---|---|
| **Variant: Ausf F** | **Armour: 35mm (1.4in) max** |
| **Crew: 3** | **Engine: Maybach HL62TR 6-cylinder** |
| **Entered service: 1936** | **petrol developing 140hp with a top** |
| **Weight: 9,650kg (9.5 tons)** | **speed of 40kph (25mph)** |
| **Dimensions:** | **Range: 200km (124 miles)** |
| **Length: 4.81m (15ft 9in)** | **Armament:** |
| **Height: 2.15m (7ft 0.6in)** | **Main: 1 x 2cm KwK30 L/55 cannon** |
| **Width: 2.28m (7ft 5.75in)** | **Secondary: 1 x 7.92mm MG34** |

from late 1942. With a top speed of 61kph (38mph), 100 were built with 20mm guns and 31 with 50mm. The Luchs saw service in both Russia and Europe.

Many of the Pzpfw II chassis were converted to become SP guns—over 1,000 ended up either as anti-tank guns using a 75mm Pak 40/2 or as SP artillery designated the *Wespe* (Wasp). Coming off the production lines from December 1942 to mid-1944, 682 were converted to become Wasps with 158 as ammunition carriers.

The PzKpfw II Ausf A was used in numbers in the early Blitzkrieg years, but by the time of Operation Barbarossa was completely outclassed.

# Char B1

## Heavy Tank | France | 1935

Conceived as an infantry tank in 1921, pushed by General Estienne, the *Char de Bataille* B was built by a consortium of French companies (AMX, FCM, Renault, Saint-Chamond and Schneider) under the code name *Tracteur 30*. The production version was named the Char B1 but after only a few had been built in 1935 the uparmoured and upgunned B1-bis replaced it on the production lines. Difficult and costly to produce, the Char B1-bis boasted 60mm (2.36in) of armour that could withstand all the German tank guns but it was slow and had poor range. On top of this, its main armament was a short-barrelled, hull-mounted 75mm gun, whose sighting and firing was controlled by the driver, who made corrections by manoeuvring the tank. On top there was a one-man 47mm-armed turret with a coaxial MG, which had to be fired by the tank commander—the practicalities of commanding and firing never being good bedfellows.

Nevertheless, in combat it proved a formidable opponent and in one classic encounter

## SPECIFICATION

**Variant: B1-bis**
**Crew: 4**
**Entered service: 1936**
**Weight: 32,500kg (32 tons)**
**Dimensions:**
**Length: 6.52m (21ft 5in)**
**Height: 2.79m (9ft 2in)**
**Width: 2.5m (8ft 2in)**

**Armour: 60mm (2.36in) max**
**Engine: Renault 6-cylinder petrol developing 300hp with a top speed of 28kph (17mph)**
**Range: 180km (112 miles)**
**Armament:**
**Main: 1 x 75mm gun, 1 x 47mm gun**
**Secondary: 2 x 7.5mm MGs**

Three Char B1-bis. The tank at left, No 372 *Vertus*, was damaged on 16 May 1940.

on 16 May 1940 at Stonne in the Ardennes, the B1-bis *Eure* commanded Captain Pierre Billotte attacked and destroyed 11 PzKpfw IIs and 2 PzKpfw IVs of 8th Panzer Regiment, in the process surviving 150 hits. After the fall of France, the Germans didn't use the Char Bs they captured as front-line tanks because of the one-man turret, but 60 were converted to flamethrowers and the others saw service if not actual combat.

Char B1-bis No 111 *Dunkerque* was destroyed on 6 June 1940 at Neuvy sur Loeilly while part of the 347th CCC (*Compagnie Autonome de Chars de Combat* - Independent Tank Company).

# Mark VI

## Light Tank | United Kingdom | 1936

In the 1920s Vickers-Armstrong produced a series of light tanks that proved to be good export sellers in the cash-strapped interwar years. Sales were made to various South American countries, Canada, Holland and Japan—and with slight modifications they were produced as the Italian CV3/33, the Russian T-27 and the Polish PK. Even the Germans took note and the PzKpfw I was based on the Vickers Light Tank. By the start of World War II, the Mk VI had seen some three years of production and over 1,000 were in service around the world. Ideal for the reconnaissance role—although all too often used in the front line as cruiser tanks with disastrous results—the British Army used the Mk VIA, VIB (simplified to ease production), VIB Indian pattern (as the VIB but without the commander's cupola) and VIC which was uparmed with 15mm and 7.92mm Besa MGs in place of the Vickers MGs. Production of the VIC ceased in 1940 and the vehicle continued to see service in the Western Desert until 1942.

## SPECIFICATION

**Variant: Mk VIB**
**Crew: 2**
**Entered service: 1937**
**Weight: 5,080kg (5 tons)**
**Dimensions:**
**Length: 4.01m (13ft 2in)**
**Height: 2.26m (7ft 5in)**
**Width: 2.08m (6ft 10m)**

**Armour: 10mm (0.4in) max**
**Engine: Meadows 6-cylinder petrol developing 88hp with a top speed 65kph (35mph)**
**Range: 209km (124 miles)**
**Armament:**
**Main: 1 x Vickers 0.50in MG**
**Secondary: 1 x Vickers 0.303in MG**

Crews race to their Mk VI light tanks.

# Sd Kfz 141 PzKpfw III

## Medium Tank | Germany | 1937

The long-awaited medium PzKpfw III, ordered in 1935, finally entered production with the Ausf E after a number of short-run development vehicles—the Ausf A, 10 of which appeared in 1936; Ausf B and C, 15 of each appearing in 1937; and Ausf D, 10 built in 1938–39. 440 Ausf E were built, with a number being upgunned from the original 37mm to a 50mm L/40 gun, which also happened on the Ausf E and F—the 50mm was the largest gun possible for the size of turret. 600 Ausf G models were produced from April 1940 onwards, some of which were tropicalised for use in North Africa. The Ausf H saw a significant increase in track width and was the first model to receive, latterly, the long-barrelled L/60 gun; the Ausf L also mounted a 5cm gun and thicker armour, whilst the Ausf M introduced *Schürzen* (skirts) to protect against HEAT weapons such as the PIAT and Bazooka. This was added to other vehicles.

The Ausf N was the last model, equipped for the close-support

| SPECIFICATION | |
|---|---|
| Variant: **Ausf J** | Engine: **Maybach HL120TRM** |
| Crew: **5** | **12-cyclinder petrol developing 300hp** |
| Entered service: **1941** | **with a top speed of 40kph (25mph)** |
| Weight: **21,845kg (18 tons)** | Range: **155km (96 miles)** |
| Dimensions: | Armament: |
| Length: **5.52m (18ft 1in)** | Main: **1 x 5cm KwK38 L/42** |
| Height: **2.5m (8ft 2.5in)** | Secondary: **1 x 7.92mm coaxial and** |
| Width: **2.95m (9ft 8in)** | **1 x 7.92mm hull-mounted MG34s** |
| Armour: **50mm (2in) max** | |

PzKpfw III Auf Js in Russia. 1,500 Js were produced March 1941–July 1942.

role with an L/24 short barrel. Withdrawn from front-line service in 1943, the PzKpfw III chassis proved a stable platform and was used for the Sturmgeschütz III assault gun. Over 6,000 PzKpfw IIIs were built, the Ausf J being the most numerous (2,616, the last 1,000 having the longer L/60 gun) and 9,400 StuG IIIs. Other versions included flamethrowers, submersibles (the *Tauchpanzer*, which was designed for use in the invasion of Britain and could spend up to 20 minutes completely submerged), command, recovery and ammunition carriers as well as the gun tanks. After its baptism of fire during the invasion of Poland—when 98 were available—the PzKpfw III served with distinction in the campaigns against Yugoslavia and Greece, and was used in numbers for Operation Barbarossa.

# Sd Kfz 161 PzKpfw IV

## Medium Tank | Germany | 1937

One of the best medium tanks of the war, the PzKpfw IV was the only German battle tank to stay in production and service throughout WWII. With a turret ring large enough to take more powerful guns, and an excellent, robust chassis the PzKpfw IV was regularly uparmoured and upgunned. As with the PzKpfw III, development was swathed in secrecy and slow: the Ausf A arrived in 1936 the B in 1937, C and D in 1938. 211 were involved in the attack on Poland; they performed well enough for the tank to be accepted as standard issue and receive its Sd Kfz 161 ordnance number, but it was realized that the tank need to be upgunned and uparmoured.

At the time of the invasion of France there were 278 available. The Ausf E was the first model to enter extended production, 100 being built.

The Ausf F was the first to be upgunned with a long-barrelled KwK 40 7.5cm gun and built in quantity—393 being produced in 1940–41, and around 600 in total, some 175 as F2s with the KwK40. A large number of the next model,

| SPECIFICATION | |
|---|---|
| **Variant: Ausf F2** | **Engine: Maybach HL120TRM** |
| **Crew: 5** | **12-cyclinder petrol developing 300hp** |
| **Entered service: 1942** | **with a top speed of 40kph (24.8mph)** |
| **Weight: 22,369kg (23 tons)** | **Range: 209km (130 miles)** |
| **Dimensions:** | **Armament:** |
| **Length: 6.62m (21ft 8in)** | **Main: 1 x 75mm KwK40 L/43** |
| **Height: 2.68m (8ft 9.5in)** | **Secondary: 1 x 7.92mm coaxial and** |
| **Width: 2.88m (9ft 5.5in)** | **1 x 7.92mm hull-mounted MG34s** |
| **Armour: 50mm (2in) max** | |

he Ausf G, was produced—over 1,700 by he end of the war. It had better transmision and thicker armour. The Ausf H was roduced in large quantities—nearly 4,000 hassis in total, although not all were gun anks. The last version was the Ausf J, veighing 25 tons, with a range of over 00km and a top speed of 38kph: 1,700 were roduced. The total number of PzKpfw V reached 8,500, one-third of Germany's otal tank production. Of these, some 75%, ,153, were lost on the Eastern Front.

Variants included 3,600 tank lestroyers including 1,980 Jagdpanzer V, the Sturmpanzer IV *Brummbär* grumpy), the *Hummel* (bumblebee) nd 1,140 StuG IVs. There were four lakpanzers—240 *Möbelwagen* (removal an), 100 *Wirbelwind* (whirlwind), 65 *Ostwind* (East wind) and 5 *Kugelblitz* ball lightning) prototypes. Conversions ncluded 105 *Panzerbefehlswagen* IV command vehicle); 40 Ds and Es ecame Tauchpanzer; the *Bergepanzer* V (ARV), the *Panzerbeobachtungswagen* V (observation tank) and various ridgelayers. Parts of the PzKpfw IV vere also used in the construction of the ak 43/1-armed *Nashorn* (Rhino) tank lestroyer and 15cm-armed Hummel P artillery.

This PzKpfw IV was knocked out during the fighting on the Brest peninsula, August 1944.

# A11 Matilda I
## and A12 Matilda II

## Infantry Tank | United Kingdom | 1938

The A11 Matilda I was an ungainly vehicle designed as the first British 'infantry' tank, an idea posited in a 1934 paper by the Inspector-General of the Royal Tanks Corps. The plan was to supply a small vehicle that could inconspicuously provide the infantry with machine-gun support. It need not be fast because it had to keep pace with the infantry,

and it needed to be cheap. The result was the Matilda I which was trialled in September 1936, ordered in 1937 and built in 1937–40, production ceasing at a total of 140. It entered service in 1938 and when it fought in France in 1940 proved to be well armoured enough to resist German anti-tank weapons, but outgunned by the oppositions tanks. The evaluation of equipment that took place after Dunkirk identified its weaknesses and it ceased production and front-line use.

The Matilda II may have had the same name but it was more closely modelled on the A7 medium tank than the A11. Although on the drawing board as early as 1936, it proved complex to manufacture, and

---

### SPECIFICATION

**Variant: Infantry Tank Mk I, Matilda I**
**Crew: 2**
**Entered service: 1938**
**Weight: 11,160kg (11 tons)**
**Dimensions:**
**Length: 4.85m (15ft 11in)**
**Height: 1.85m (6ft 1in)**

**Width: 2.29m (7ft 6in)**
**Armour: 60mm (2.4in) max**
**Engine: Ford V8 petrol developing 70hp with a top speed of 13kph (8mph)**
**Range: 129km (80 miles)**
**Armament: 1 x 0.50in or 0.303in MG**

---

# A11 MATILDA I AND A12 MATILDA II

The first Matilda lacked hitting power and production ended after Dunkirk.

production did not start until 1938. Only two vehicles were available at the start of the war but when production ceased in August 1943, nearly 3,000 had been built and the Matilda had earned the title, albeit for only a brief time, of 'Queen of the Battlefield'. Its first action was in France in the face of the German Blitzkrieg, where it proved immune to German anti-tank weapons. Matilda Is and IIs formed the bulk of the 74 tanks that counterattacked Rommel's Panzers on 21 May 1940 at Arras. The Germans repulsed the attack thanks to the mighty Flak 88 used in the ground role and Luftwaffe air support, but the attack frightened the Germans enough to halt their attack and gave time for Operation Dynamo.

The story was the same in the desert of North Africa where 7th Royal Tank Regiment's Matilda IIs were instrumental in defeating the Italian Army. Following the arrival of the DAK in mid-1941, with its better armed Panzers and its 88s, use of the Matilda in North Africa tailed off. It could not remain a gun tank because its turret was too small to be upgunned so it was modified for other uses. 32 Matilda flails were used to clear minefields before El Alamein; others became flamethrowers, minerollers or bridgelayers and ensured the Matilda was the only British vehicle that served throughout the war.

The Matilda II's protection was excellent and it was almost immune to Italian tanks and anti-tank weapons when they met in the North African desert.

# KV series

## Heavy Tank | USSR | 1939

The Russian KV series of heavy tanks, named after the Soviet defence minister Kliment Voroshilov, began their development in the mid-1930s as alternatives to the T-100 and SMK heavy tanks—bunker-busting monsters, able to dominate a battlefield without moving around very much. Considering the T-100's history of automotive problems and continued mechanical unreliability they certainly succeeded. It was a beast of vehicle to handle, had an ancient transmission system and its massive weight precluded it from crossing many bridges. It was two-turreted with a 76.2mm on top and a 45mm below. Adding extra armour over time without upgrading the engine only compounded the problem.

The Heavy Tank Design team headed by Lt-Col Kotin, started working on two single-turreted tanks to be armed with either a 76.2mm (KV-1) or 152mm (KV-2) main armament. In 1939 the KV-1 outperformed the T-100 and SMK during trials and was tested in combat

| SPECIFICATION | |
|---|---|
| **Variant: KV-1 Model** | **Armour: 90mm (3.5in) max** |
| **Crew: 5** | **Engine: Model V-2 V12 diesel developing 600hp with a top speed of 35kph (22mph)** |
| **Entered service: 1941** | |
| **Weight: 45,000kg (44.3 tons)** | |
| **Dimensions:** | **Range: 335km (208 miles)** |
| **Length: 6.75m (22ft 2in)** | **Armament:** |
| **Width: 3.32m (10ft 11in)** | **Main: 1 x 76.2mm M1941 ZiS-5 gun** |
| **Height: 2.71m (8ft 11in)** | **Secondary: 3 or 4 × 7.62mm DT MGs** |

Abandoned KV-2, June 1941.

blank range. The Germans produced a detailed report on the Russian tanks which led to improved armaments: by 1942 the Germans had heavier 50mm and 75mm weaponry. This, combined with the fact that the KV series was more expensive to produce than the T-34 but had the same calibre gun, plus the fluid and fast moving nature of the war, signalled the winding

during the Winter War, entering production in December.

By the time of Barbarossa, the German invasion of Russia in 1941, the Soviets had the KV-1 and a few KV-2s. The Germans were surprised by the KV-1, for its armour made it virtually impenetrable by the panzers except at point-

down of KV production in 1943 after 4,736 had been built.

The last KV prototypes were used to start a new heavy tank programme, to combat the German Panther and Tiger. By then Voroshilov had been replaced and this new AFV was named after the boss himself: Joseph Stalin.

The KV-1 was let down by unreliable transmission.

# A22 Mk IV Churchill

## Infantry Tank | United Kingdom | 1941

The Churchill was the fourth of the British infantry tanks, preceded by the Matilda I and II and the Valentine. Designed when war broke out under the misapprehension that the fighting would soon bog down into trench warfare, it started life armed with a 2pdr in the turret and a close-support 3in howitzer in the hull. The prototypes appeared in June 1940 around the same time as the debacle in France that left Britain with fewer than 100 tanks to defend against invasion. Production of the Mk I, a scaled-down version of the prototype built by Vauxhall, was hurried through and the first vehicles were delivered in June 1941.

The problems associated with the speed of this production were apparent from the start and the Churchill was plagued by teething troubles that required Vauxhall engineers to be seconded to units equipped with the tanks. There were numerous reworkings including a new 6pdr-armed turret on the Mk III. Although seriously undergunned when compared to German tanks, it had excellent armour protection and good cross-country agility and performed well in combat—although this seemed unlikely to the Germans who assessed vehicles captured on Dieppe beach reporting that: 'The vehicle offers nothing worthy of consideration by technical personnel, nor has it any new constructive features either in the metallurgical field, or in the field of weapon technology.' The 3in howitzer was 'bad and old fashioned'; the 2pdr was 'left behind both in construction and effectiveness' while the 6pdr's performance 'does not approach that of Russian guns of the same calibre.'

However, it was in 1944 when Churchill's finest hour approached that it proved itself an adaptable platform for the specialised roles necessary for the amphibious invasion of Europe. Many of the 79th Armoured Division's Funnies were based on the Churchill: the Crocodile flamethrower, the AVRE (Armoured Vehicle Royal Engineers) armed with a 290mm Petard mortar that fired the 'Flying Dustbin' 40lb (18kg) projectile, the Ark bridge carrier and the various mat layers such as Bobbin and Twin Bobbin.

**A22 MK IV CHURCHILL**

Churchill Mk IV with short-barrelled 6pdr main gun.

# M3/M5 Stuart

## Light Tank | USA | 1941

**O**bsolete by 1940, the M2 series—the predecessor of the M3—was produced in 1936–37. The last model, the M2A4, formed the basis of the M3, which was designed in 1940, informed by the events in Europe. One important change was improved armour which improved protection but increased its weight and required improved suspension.

Nicknamed 'The Honey' for its handling qualities, the M3 first saw action with the British in North Africa as the Stuart I. (84 vehicles were included in the first Lend-Lease shipment in July 1941.) The first M3 models (5,811 produced) were riveted, carried side-sponson MGs, and had both petrol and diesel engine variants. The next model, the M3A1 (4,621 built; in British service Stuart III and IV depending on engine) lost the side-sponson MGs and commander's cupola and gained power traverse for the turret. The final model, the M3A3 (3,427 built; Stuart V),

## SPECIFICATION

**Variant: M3**
**Crew: 4**
**Entered service: 1941**
**Weight: 12,428kg (12.2 tons)**
**Dimensions:**
**Length: 4.83m (14ft 11in)**
**Height: 2.52m (8ft 3in)**
**Width: 2.23m (7ft 4in)**
**Armour: 51mm (2in) max**
**Engine: Continental W670**

**7-cylinder petrol developing 250hp or Guiberson T1020 9-cylinder diesel developing 340hp with a top speed of 58kph (36mph)**
**Range: 120km (75 miles)**
**Armament:**
**Main: 1 x 37mm M5 or M6 gun**
**Secondary: 5 x 0.30in Browning M1919 MGs (1 x coaxial, 1 x AA, 1 x hull-mounted, 2 x sponson-mounted)**

had a larger turret, a redesigned hull, extra fuel tanks and ammunition stowage.

The M5 (in British service the Stuart VI) was first produced in March 1942. Still under-gunned with only a 37mm gun, the main difference between the two types was that the M5 had twin Cadillac engines that required the rear of the hull to be stepped. It gradually replaced the M3 in production from 1942 and was, in turn, succeeded by the M24 Chaffee in 1944.

The M3/M5 was produced in great numbers (over 25,000) and remained in service well after the end of the war. The main variant of the M5 was the M8 howitzer motor carriage armed with a 75mm—1,776 were built September 1942–January 1944.

The M8 howitzer motor carriage saw the Stuart chassis wedded to a 75mm in an open turret.

ne of the recognition features of the M5 Stuart is its rear hull, stepped to accommodate the twin Cadillac engines.

# M3 General Lee/ General Grant

## Medium Tank | USA | 1941

When the M3 medium arrived in North Africa it was greeted warmly by the British. The side-sponson mounted 75mm gun gave the Eighth Army a tank that could at last compete with the German PzKpfw IIIs and IVs. The Lend-Lease vehicles arrived in time for the battle of Gazala in May 1942 and—along with the M4 medium—contributed materially to the defeat of the DAK in North Africa.

There were five main US versions of the M3: the first version, 4,924 produced April–August 1941, had a riveted hull and a Wright radial engine. The M3A1, 300 produced February–August 1942, a cast hull; the M3A2, with its all-welded hull, had only just entered production when the engine was changed to twin GM 6-71 diesel engines and the designation changed to M3A3. 322 were built March–December 1942. The M3A4 was the M3 with a Chrysler A-57 engine—109 produced June–August 1942. Finally, the M3A5 was as the M3A3 but with a riveted hull. 591 were

| SPECIFICATION | |
|---|---|
| **Variant: Grant I (British M3 with redesigned turret)** | **Armour: 37mm (1.5in)** |
| **Entered service: 1942** | **Engine: Wright Continental R975 9-cylinder petrol developing 340hp with a top speed of 42kph (26mph)** |
| **Crew: 6** | |
| **Weight: 29,465kg (29 tons)** | **Range: 193km (120 miles)** |
| **Dimensions:** | **Armament:** |
| **Length: 5.64m (18ft 6in)** | **Main: 1 x 75mm M2 or M3 gun** |
| **Height: 2.84m (9ft 4in)** | **Secondary: 1 x 37mm M5 or M6 gun** |
| **Width: 2.72m (8ft 11in)** | **and 4 x .30in Browning M1919 MGs** |

The M3 General Lee: note riveted construction, side doors and commander's cupola.

built January–November 1942.

Initially, the British had their own version of the M3: known as the General Grant it benefited from battle experience and had a number of modifications, the main one being a different, lower and longer turret that reduced the silhouette, cut the crew to four and had room for the radio in the bustle. It was this version that was shipped to the Eighth Army in early 1942. Other versions of the US M3 in service with the British were called the General Lee, and 250 of these reached North Africa by the time of El Alamein, a total of 600 reaching the desert. These were subsequently used in Burma.

There were a number of M3 variants that saw combat: the M31 ARV, M33 prime mover, and the M7 HMC—the Priest in British service—that was based on the M3's chassis.

# T-34 series

## Medium Tank | USSR | 1941

**O**ne of the outstanding tanks of World War II and one of the most produced of all time, the T-34—like the US M4 Sherman for the Western allies—was the mainstay of the Soviet armed forces throughout the conflict. It possessed the best balance of the three main characteristics of an AFV, having a fantastic blend of speed, firepower and protection with its sloped armour. The Germans, who had no prior knowledge of it until it appeared on the battlefield in 1941, were deeply impressed and learned to fear its performance and firepower: it mounted a 76.2mm high velocity main gun and its wide tracks gave it excellent cross-country capability. In response they went on to develop the Panther.

Again as with the Sherman, once the Soviets had perfected the basic design they refined it and produced the T-34 in massive numbers—53,536 were produced during WWII. Surprisingly, the T-34's beginning was not particularly auspicious, as automotive problems combined with poor crew training and leadership led to huge

| SPECIFICATION | |
|---|---|
| **Variant: T-34/76 Model 1941** | **Armour: 60mm (2.4in)** |
| **Crew: 4** | **Engine: V-2-34 38.8-litre V12 diesel** |
| **Entered service: 1940** | **developing 500hp with a top speed of** |
| **Weight: 26,520kg (26.1 tons)** | **50kph (31mph)** |
| **Dimensions:** | **Range: 400km (250 miles)** |
| **Length: 6.68m (21ft 11in)** | **Armament:** |
| **Width: 3.00m (9ft 10in)** | **Main: 1 x 76.2mm F-34 tank gun** |
| **Height: 2.45m (8ft)** | **Secondary: 2 × 7.62mm DT MGs** |

losses; but the Russians learnt quickly and soon were able to bring their numerical superiority to bear and developed their swamping tactics to cope with German tactical superiority. In 1943 the T-34/85 emerged, heavier and more powerful than its predecessor, with thicker armour and a new hexagonal turret armed with a new 85mm main gun; it would be produced for the rest of the war and afterwards was exported worldwide. Many variants were also made, including tank destroyers, self-propelled howitzers, mine clearers and recovery vehicles. T-34s were even built into fixed fortifications as strongpoints.

T-34/76As of the Third Belorussian Front (Front in the Russian Forces is the equivalent of Army Group) in 1944.

This T34/85, seen in Berlin in April 1945, bears the name of poet Vladimir Mayakovsky.

# M4 Sherman

## Medium Tank | USA | 1942

The US M4 Sherman ranks as one of the most successful tanks of all time, with almost 50,000 vehicles produced, making it the most widely used AFV by the United States and all the other Western Allies during WWII, as well as updated versions seeing action into the late 20th century in the Korean, Arab-Israeli and Indo-Pakistani wars. Perhaps the key reasons for its success was precisely this numerical superiority, attained through sticking to a good basic design which was easy to produce, made of standardised parts that combined mechanical reliability with ease of maintenance. This versatility also enabled the chassis to be used in many variants including tank destroyers, hull-mounted rocket launchers, self-propelled artillery, flame-throwers and minesweepers as well as turretless battlefield taxis, ambulances and specialist repair and recovery vehicles.

Evolved from the M3 Medium, the Sherman mounted a gyro-stabilised 75mm main gun in a central fully traversing turret.

<table>
<tr><td colspan="2">SPECIFICATION</td></tr>
<tr><td>Variant: M4A3</td><td>Engine: Ford GAA-111 8-cylinder petrol developing 450hp with a top speed of 48kph (30mph)</td></tr>
<tr><td>Crew: 5</td><td></td></tr>
<tr><td>Entered service: 1942</td><td></td></tr>
<tr><td>Weight: 36,577kg (36 tons)</td><td>Range: 240km (150 miles)</td></tr>
<tr><td>Dimensions:</td><td>Armament:</td></tr>
<tr><td>Length: 7.5m (24ft 8in)</td><td>Main: 1 x 76mm M1 gun</td></tr>
<tr><td>Height: 2.95m (9ft 8in)</td><td>Secondary: 2 x 0.30in Browning M1919A4</td></tr>
<tr><td>Width: 2.7m (8ft 9in)</td><td>MGs (coaxial and hull-mounted), 1 x 0.50</td></tr>
<tr><td>Armour: 60mm (2.36in)</td><td>Browning M2HB AA MG</td></tr>
</table>

The US Army used the 76mm M1 gun to improve the M4's anti-tank abilities—as here for the lead vehicle. Note also the wheels and tracks on the front glacis. There was no scientific proof that this helped add protection, but psychology played its part.

# M4 SHERMAN

A column of British tanks in July 1944. In the lead, a Sherman VC Firefly showing off the long barrel and muzzle brake of the 17pdr main gun. It was the Allied tank most capable of taking on German Tigers and Panthers but was issued at only one per troop because there were so few.

## SPECIFICATION

**Variant: M50 Israeli Upgraded Sherman**
**Crew: 5**
**Entered service: 1964**
**Weight: 39,625kg (39 tons)**
**Dimensions:**
**Length: 5.89m (19ft 4in)**
**Height: 2.75m (9ft)**
**Width: 2.62m (8ft 7in)**

**Armour: 76mm (3in)**
**Powerplant: Cummins diesel developing 460hp with a top speed of 45kph (28mph)**
**Range: 270km (168 miles)**
**Armament:**
**Main: French CN 75-50 75mm gun (later French 105mm Modèle F1)**
**Secondary: 2 x 0.30in and 1 x 0.50in MGs**

There were six main types: the M4 (6,748 built from July 1942); M4A1—first production model from February 1942, as M4 but with a cast hull (6,281 built); M4A2—as M4 but with twin GM diesel engines, this version was used by the USMC and lend-lease (8,053 built from April 1942); M4A3 had a Ford GAA V8 petrol engine and was mainly used by the US Army (3,071 built from June 1942); M4A4 followed on from M4 production with three-piece bolted nose and a Chrysler WC Multibank engine which required hull lengthening (7,499 built from July 1942); M4A6 final model with Caterpillar RD-1280 radial diesel engine, it was produced following on from the M4A4 (only 75 built but orders cancelled to standardise engines).

First used in North Africa, the M4 was superior to the PzKpfw IIIs and IVs and infinitely superior to any Japanese armour it came across. However, it was not developed to take on the next generation tanks that it met in Europe—indeed, production of the M4 Sherman was favoured over the heavier M26 Pershing which might have provided more competition. Instead, although all-arms tactics helped, the M4 was outgunned and vulnerable to later German tanks such as the Panther and Tiger and it suffered heavy casualties until the British Firefly (with a 17pdr) and the later variants mounting an improved high-velocity 76mm gun went some way towards redressing the balance. Later in the war, tank destroyer units were formed featuring the M36 which was based on the M4 hull and chassis.

Post-WWII the continuous Cold War development of tanks meant the Sherman was used only by emerging countries, primarily in the Middle East and South America. Israel was the

The 'Calliope' rocket launcher attached 60 4.5in rocket launching tubes to an M4 Sherman. Traverse was achieved by moving the turret; elevation by the rod attached to the main armament.

largest user, purchasing old Shermans for her early defence, then modifying them to extend their working life with new track components and a new suspension system, and an improved diesel engine, while the M4A1 Sherman mantlet was increased in size to take the British 105mm L7 main gun, along with a new fire control system and night vision equipment. So despite its vulnerable high silhouette the Sherman's mechanical reliability and numbers ensured it enjoyed a long and successful career.

# Sd Kfz 181 PzKpfw VI Tiger Ausf H*

## and Sd Kfz 182 Tiger Ausf B

## Heavy Tank | Germany | 1942

**I**ts name and prowess belie its numbers. Fewer than 1,400 Tigers and 500 Tiger IIs were built, but from the first they were recognised as the ultimate opponent—a fact that German propaganda did much to amplify and has fostered the belief in German WWII weaponry as having outstripped its adversaries. The requirement for a heavy tank had been identified in the late 1930s and a competition between Henschel and Porsche prototypes was held on Hitler's birthday, 20 April 1942 at his headquarters at Rastenburg. The Henschel vehicle won, so the 90 Porsche vehicles in hand were converted to become the Sd Kfz 184 Panzerjäger Tiger, originally named Ferdinand and later Elefant.

*In February 1944 the Tiger designation Ausf H was changed to PzKpfw Tiger Ausf E.*

| SPECIFICATION | |
|---|---|
| **Variant: Tiger I Ausf E** | **Armour: 100mm (3.9in) max** |
| **Crew: 5** | **Engine: Maybach HL210P45 12-cyl-** |
| **Entered service: 1942** | **inder petrol developing 700hp with** |
| **Weight: 56.900kg (56 ton)** | **a top speed of 37kph (23mph)** |
| **Dimensionsz** | **Range: 140km (87 miles)** |
| **Length: 8.45m (27ft 8.5in)** | **Armament:** |
| **Height: 3m (9ft 10in)** | **Main: 1 x 8.8cm KwK36 L/56** |
| **Width: 3.56m (11ft 3.8in)** | **Secondary: 1 x 7.92mm coaxial and** |
| | **1 x 7.92mm hull-mounted MG34s** |

Loading ammunition.

Postwar view of a Tiger I with a snorkel about to be tested by the British.

Production of the Tiger I began in July 1942 and it first saw action in Russia in August 1942. With significant armour and the powerful 88mm KwK36 L/56 gun that could penetrate 112mm (4in) of armour at 500m (550 yards), Tiger could knock out most Allied tanks at distance with little fear of reprisal. However, it did have weak points: the overlapping road wheels could get packed with mud and debris which, when frozen, could immobilise the tank; the turret traverse was slow; the 650hp V12 Maybach engine was unreliable and led to many breakdowns; the extreme weight ensured that recovery of immobilised vehicles was difficult in combat leading to the loss of only lightly damaged or broken down tanks. It could also be knocked out by a resolute enemy: the first use of Tigers in both Russia and Tunisia saw them knocked out by anti-tank guns at close range. Nevertheless, on the Eastern Front and in the defence of Normandy it proved formidable as Wittmann proved at Villers-Bocage (see page 56). Variants included two command vehicles (Sd Kfz 267/268 Panzerbefehlswagen Tiger), a recovery vehicle (a field modification created by removing an Ausf E's main armament) and the remarkable Sturmtiger or Sturmmöser which mounted a 38cm Raketenwerfer 61. Ten Tigers became Sturmmörser in late 1944.

Tiger Ausf E was followed by the Tiger Ausf B, better known as the Tiger II or Königstiger. Entering production in late 1943, only 483 of this powerful 68-ton heavy tank were built. It first saw action on the Eastern Front in May 1944 and in France in August. Armed with a 88mm KwK 43 L/71 main gun—almost 6.5m (21ft) long—initially in turrets planned for use in the Porsche Tiger, subsequently in a modified turret, it also suffered from the Tiger I's automotive unreliability.

A few Tiger IIs were converted to command tanks, but the main variant was the Sd Kfz 186 Jagdtiger. 70 of these were built, some with the 128mm Pak 80 L/55 as main armament—the most powerful tank gun of the war—others with the equally powerful Pak 44, and still others with the Pak 43/3 used on the Jagdpanther.

## SPECIFICATION

| | |
|---|---|
| **Variant: Tiger II** | **Engine: Maybach HL230P30 12-cylinder petrol developing 6900hp with a top speed of 35kph (22mph)** |
| **Crew: 5** | |
| **Entered service: 1944** | |
| **Weight: 69,091kg (68 tons)** | **Range: 170km (105 miles)** |
| **Dimensions:** | **Armament:** |
| **Length: 10.3m (33ft 10in)** | **Main: 1 x 8.8cm KwK43 L/71** |
| **Height: 3m (9ft 10in)** | **Secondary: 1 x 7.92mm coaxial and** |
| **Width: 3.76m (12ft 4in)** | **1 x 7.92mm hull-mounted MG34s** |
| **Armour: 180mm (7.4in) max** | |

This Königstiger has a Henschel turret housing an 88mm main gun with a two-piece barrel. Note the wide battle tracks and armoured skirting. It was knocked out at La Gleize in Belgium, today the site of an excellent museum.

# A27M Cruiser Mk VIII Cromwell

## Cruiser Tank | United Kingdom | 1943

On 13 June 1944 at Villers-Bocage in Normandy, Michael Wittmann, CO of 2nd Company, 101st SS Heavy Tank Battalion, mauled the 22nd Armoured Brigade, part of the famous 7th Armoured Division. The Desert Rats had re-equipped when they had returned from Italy to take part in the battle for Normandy exchanging their M4 Shermans for a new tank, the Cromwell: they lost at least 16 of them during the engagement. While one firefight is too specific to generalise from, there's no doubt that the men who had to fight in the Cromwell thought it undergunned—both its 6pdr and, later 75mm, wasn't a match for the main gun of the late model PzKpfw IVs, Panthers or Tigers—and underarmoured.

As with most British tanks of the period, Cromwell was too narrow to take a larger turret with a bigger gun: the loading gauge of Britain's railways precluded wider vehicles. However

## SPECIFICATION

**Crew: 5**

**Entered service: 1943**

**Weight: 27,941kg (27.5 tons)**

**Dimensions:**

**Length: 6.35m (20ft 10in)**

**Height: 2.49m (8ft 2in)**

**Width: 2.9m (9ft 6in)**

**Armour: 76mm (3in);**

**101mm (4in) with appliqué**

**Engine: Rolls-Royce Meteor V12 petrol developing 600hp with a top speed of 64kph (40mph), reduced to 52kph (32mph) from the Mk IV**

**Range: 278km (173 miles)**

**Armament:**

**Main: Mks I–III—1 x 6pdr; Mks IV, V, VII—75mm, Mks VI, VIII—95mm howitzer**

**Secondary: 1 or 2 x 7.92mm Besa MGs**

Cromwell armed with a 75mm main gun and hull-mounted Besa 7.92mm MG.

what the Cromwell did have was speed and reliability. The M in its A27M designation stands for Meteor because the Cromwell's engine was adapted from the famous Merlin aircraft engine giving the tank a top speed of 40mph, although this was reduced to 32mph from late Mk IVs onwards to reduce track damage. This speed stood the British in good stead as the Allies advanced across Europe towards Germany, leaving the constrictions of the bocage country behind enabling the Cromwell to come into its own.

# JS series

## Heavy Tank | USSR | 1943

The Soviet heavy tank programme entered a new phase in 1941 with the development of the JS series, using experience gained from the battlefield and the KV series. The new requirement was—as always—for a larger main gun capable of taking on the new German Panther and Tiger heavy tanks and as a bunker buster. The JS-1 appeared in 1943. It used the chassis of the KV as a starting point; a larger superstructure was designed with a new turret mounting a 100mm main gun. With a new V2-IS 12-cylinder diesel engine the JS-1 was considerably more mechanically reliable than the old KV series and the following year saw the introduction of the slightly larger and heavier JS-2, mounting the 122mm main gun that made it the most powerful MBT in the world at that time. The JS-2 became known as the Victory Tank to the Soviets, who used it in the battle of Berlin. It certainly impressed the Western Allies and led to the development of their own heavy tank programmes.

Too late for WWII came the 50-ton JS-3, with improved

| SPECIFICATION | |
|---|---|
| **Variant: JS-1** | **Armour: Maximum: 132mm (5.2in)** |
| **Crew: 4** | **Engine: V-2-IS 12-cylinder diesel** |
| **Entered service: 1943** | **developing 510hp with a top speed of** |
| **Weight: 46.000kg (45.3 tons)** | **37kph (23mph)** |
| **Dimensions:** | **Range: 250km (155 miles)** |
| **Length: 8.32m (27ft 3in)** | **Armament:** |
| **Height: 2.9m (9ft 6in)** | **Main: 1 x D5-T 85mm gun** |
| **Width: 3.25m (10ft 8in)** | **Secondary: 3 x DT 7.62mm (0.3in) MGs** |

JS-2s enter Berlin in 1945.

armour and the impressive D-25 L/43 122mm main gun, but now fitted into a new compact mushroom-shaped turret that would become a hallmark of Cold War Soviet tanks. Its other distinctive feature was its glacis plate bow which came to a point in the middle, and earned the nickname of 'the Pike'. The JS-3 was sold abroad to China, Cuba, Egypt, North Korea and many Warsaw Pact countries. It scared the West when seen at the Victory Day Parade in Belin and led to heavy tank programmes that produced the American M103 and British Conqueror.

By 1948 the final version of the JS series weighed over 68 tons and mounted a 150mm main gun, but its huge weight and size ensured it never went into production.

## SPECIFICATION

**Variant: JS-2 Model 1944**
**Crew: 4**
**Entered service: 1944**
**Weight: 46,000kg (45 tons)**
**Dimensions:**
**Length: 9.9m (32ft 6in)**
**Height 2.73m (8ft 11in)**
**Width: 3.09m (10ft 2in)**
**Armour: 120mm (4.72in) max**

**Engine: V-2-IS 12-cylinder diesel developing 513hp with a top speed of 37kph (23mph)**
**Range: 240km (150 miles)**
**Armament:**
**Main: D25-T 122mm gun**
**Secondary: 1 x DShK 12.7mm (0.50in) and 3 x DT 7.62mm (0.3in) MGs**

JS-2 in action (battle of Budapest).

**Variant: JS-3**
**Crew: 4**
**Entered service: 1945**
**Weight: 46,250kg (45.8 tons)**
**Dimensions:**
**Length: 6.81m (22ft 4in)**
**Height: 2.93m (8ft 11in)**
**Width: 3.44m (10ft 6in)**
**Armour: 230mm (9in) max**

**Engine: V-2-IS 12-cylinder diesel delivering 520hp with a top speed of 37kph (23mph)**
**Range: 209km (130 miles)**
**Armament:**
**Main: 1 x D25-T 122mm gun**
**Secondary: 1 x DShK 12.7mm (0.50in) and 3 x DT 7.62mm (0.3in) MGs**

A Soviet JS-3 heavy tank.

The JS-3 (postwar codenamed 'Pike' by NATO) arrived into service too late to see action, but made a stir when it appeared at the Allied 7 September 1945 victory parade.

# Sd Kfz 171 PzKpfw V* Panther

## Medium/Heavy Tank | Germany | 1943

**G**eneral Heinz Guderian summed up the most significant battlefield problem affecting the German forces in Russia following Operation Barbarossa in 1941 in his autobiography: 'Numerous Russian T-34s went into action and inflicted heavy losses on the German tanks ... Up to this time we had enjoyed tank superiority, but from now on the situation was reversed ... I made a report on the situation ... I described in plain terms the marked superiority of the T-34 ... I concluded by urging a commission.' The subsequent detailed study of the Soviet T-34 and KV series of tanks led to the production of the Panther, one of the best tanks of WWII. From this came the VK.3002 requirement and a competition that pitched Daimler-Benz against MAN to produce a design, MAN's coming out on top. A prototype was hurried through, completed in September 1942, and production began in early 1943.

*\* Hitler decreed on 27 February 1944 that the numeral should be dropped from the designation.*

## SPECIFICATION

**Variant: Ausf G**
**Crew: 5**
**Entered service: 1944**
**Weight: 46,230kg (45.5 tons)**
**Dimensions:**
**Length: 8.86m (29ft 1in)**
**Height: 2.98m (9ft 9in)**
**Width: 3.43m (11ft 3in)**
**Armour: 110mm (4in)**

**Engine: Maybach HL230P30 12-cylinder petrol developing 700hp with a top speed of 46kph (28.5mph)**
**Range: 322km (200 miles)**
**Armament:**
**Main: 1 x 75mm KwK42 L/70**
**Secondary: 1 x 7.92mm coaxial and 1 x 7.92mm hull-mounted MG34s**

The Panther was the best medium tank of the war. Note the driver's vision port and MG flap on the glacis plate of this Ausf D. The Ausf A introduced a ball mount for the hull machine gun and the vision port was deleted on the final model, the Ausf G.

On 5 July 1943 the Panther saw action for the first time at the battle of Kursk. The speed of development meant that early models were plagued by problems: more Panthers succumbed to mechanical issues than the enemy. However, these were ironed out and by 1944 the Panther was a feared adversary. Lighter than the Tiger, with better frontal armour and an excellent gun, the Panther's open-country, long-range performance was excellent. At close quarters, poor side armour meant it could be vulnerable to both tanks and infantry.

The first full production type was the Ausf D, 850 of which were built. It had a top speed of 45kph (28mph) and a 75mm KwK42 L/70 gun initially with a single-baffle muzzle brake, latterly replaced by a double. Later versions had Schürzen and Zimmerit anti-magnetic paste, giving it the characteristic corrugated look up close. The Ausf D was, oddly, followed by the Ausf A, 2,000 of which were built between August 1943 and May 1944. The final version was the Ausf G which benefited from combat experiences and was a formidable opponent as the Allies found out in Normandy.

The Jagdpanther tank destroyer mounted a Pak 43/3 L/71 88mm gun with a six-man crew including two loaders and a gunner. Production started in February 1944 and 382 had been built on Ausf G chassis by war's end. Other variants included a recovery vehicle (Sd Kfz 179 Bergepanther, 279 built), command vehicles (Sd Kfz 267/268 Befehlspanzer Panther), and the artillery OP vehicle (Sd Kfz 172 Beobachtungspanzer Panther).

# M24 Chaffee

## Light Tank | USA | 1944

**A** significant improvement on the M5 light, the M24 was named in honour of General Adna Chaffee, the 'Father of the US Armored Force.' After the weak 37mm of the M5, the 75mm M6 main armament (adapted from the aircraft cannon used in the B-25G) provided a real punch.

Pilot models were delivered in October 1943 and led to an immediate order for 1,000 later increased to 5,000. 4,415 of the type had been delivered by war's end, the first reaching combat units in late 1944. This number includes three SP guns: the M19 GMC—with a twin 40mm M2 AA mount, 285 had been completed by the end of the war; the M41 'Gorilla' HMC, sporting a 155 M1 howitzer, 60 completed by war's end; the M37 HMC with a 105mm M4 howitzer, 316 completed most after the end of the war. The M24 remained the standard US light tank long after the end of the war, was produced in AA and mortar carriage variants, and saw service in Korea in the 1950s, where it contributed materially to holding the attacking North Koreans at the Pusan Perimeter.

## SPECIFICATION

**Crew: 4 or 5**
**Entered service: 1944**
**Weight: 18,371kg (18 tons)**
**Dimensions:**
**Length: 5.49m (18ft)**
**Height: 2.46m (8ft 1in)**
**Width: 2.95m (9ft 8in)**
**Armour: Maximum: 38mm (1.5in)**

**Engine: 2 x Cadillac 44T24 V8, each developing 110hp with a top speed of 55kph (34mph)**
**Range: 281km (175 miles)**
**Armament:**
**Main: 1 x 75mm M6 gun**
**Secondary: 1 x Browning 0.50in MG, 1 x Browning M1919 0.30in MG**

The M24 Chaffee was the best light tank of the war and continued in US Army service until replaced by the M41 Walker Bulldog.

# M26 Pershing

## Heavy Tank | USA | 1945

**D**evelopment of a US heavy tank had stalled with the M6, trialled in 1941–42. Only 40 of these tanks were built and it never saw combat, a victim both of the cuts to tank production enforced by the new September 1942 Army Supply Program and by the defects of its design. Instead, the T26 medium tank was redesignated as a heavy tank in June 1944, and

the end result was the M26 Pershing, although politics between the Ordnance Department and Army Ground Forces led to delays.

In Europe, however, US armoured forces had felt the impact of the German heavy tanks in the Ardennes and the American General Staff rushed the 20 T26E3 pilot models into theatre for testing. They were issued to 3rd and 9th Armoured Divisions and were quickly found to be close to the Tiger and Panther although unreliable automotively. While the M26's 90mm M3 gun didn't supply the punch of an 88mm, it was still a cut above the 76mm and was instrumental in knocking out a number of Tigers and Panthers (see photo page 7), as well as supporting troops dur-

| SPECIFICATION | |
|---|---|
| Crew: **5** | Engine: **Ford GAF V8 developing 500hp** |
| Entered service: **1944** | **with a top speed of 32kph (20mph)** |
| Weight: **41,891kg (41.2 tons)** | Range: **160km (100 miles)** |
| Dimensions: | Armament: |
| Length: **8.65m (28ft 4.5in)** | Main: **1 x 90mm M3 gun** |
| Height: **2.78m (9ft 1in)** | Secondary: **2 x Browning M1919** |
| Width: **3.51m (11ft 6in)** | **0.30in MGs, 1 x Browning 0.50in** |
| Armour: Maximum: **102mm (4in)** | **AA MG** |

The M26 Pershing saw service in Europe in the last weeks of the war.

ing the attack on the bridge over the Rhine at Remagen. In total 310 reached NW Europe before war's end, including one 'Super Pershing' with extra glacis and front turret armour. Only this vehicle and the first 20 saw action in Europe.

The Pershing was rushed into production, and some 1,400 were manufactured by June 1945, some reaching Okinawa in the Pacific just as the fighting ended. Total production was 2,212. In 1948 the M26 was significantly modified with an improved engine and transmission. This and other modifications led it to be reclassified M46. 1,160 of the M26s were rebuilt: 800 to the M46 standard, 360 to M46A1.

It was in Korea that the M26 faced its greatest test, 309 being rushed there in 1950 along with the improved M46 Patton. Both tanks proved significantly better in action against the T-34/85, but the M26 was ill-suited to the Korean terrain and all of them were withdrawn during 1951 being replaced with M4A3s and M46s. Many of these vehicles went to Europe where they were replaced in 1952–53 by the M47 Patton. In 1952, 436 M26 and M26A1s were provided to the Belgian Army.

# A34 Comet

## Cruiser Tank | United Kingdom | 1945

The British finally produced a decent tank by matching a decent gun—a compact version of the 17pdr, the Vickers 77mm—with advanced British APDS ammunition and an uparmoured Cromwell. With all-welded construction, stronger suspension than the Cromwell, a cast gun mantlet and improvements to the turret traversing system, the Comet was some 5 tons heavier than the last uparmoured version of

Cromwell, although it retained many similar features and components, and the same general layout. Production began in late 1944, and some vehicles were issued in December but the first significant deliveries were to 11th Armoured Division after the Rhine crossing in March 1945. 1,200 had been produced by war's end and the Comet remained in service into the 1960s.

## SPECIFICATION

Crew: **5**
Entered service: **1945**
Weight: **35,560kg (35 tons)**
Dimensions:
Length: **7.66m (25ft 1.5in)**
Height: **2.68m (8ft 9.5in)**
Width: **3.05m (10ft)**

Armour: **101mm (4in)**
Engine: **Rolls-Royce Meteor V12 petrol developing 600hp with a top speed of 47kph (29mph)**
Range: **198km (123 miles)**
Armament: Main: **77mm gun**
Secondary: **2 x 7.92mm MGs**

Loading 77 mm HV gun ammunition.

At last! A decent British tank. The Comet put right the problems of the Cromwell and provided a gun tank that was fast, reliable and well-armed.

# A41 Centurion

## Medium Gun Tank | United Kingdom | 1945

**P**roduced just too late to see action at the end of World War II, the Centurion was a significant step up in British tank design. Started in 1943 and incorporating all the hard-won experience of four years of war, from its sloped glacis, to improve frontal protection, to the hull that was boat-shaped to improve its anti-mine capabilities, the Centurion was carefully considered. 20 pilot models were ordered, armed with 17pdr main guns and either Polsten cannon or Besa MGs mounted coaxially. The Mk II was the first production model and incorporated improvements that included a cast turret and commander's vision cupola. The Mk 3, by this time armed with a 20pdr main gun and boasting automatic gun stabilisation and ammunition storage below the turret ring, was produced from 1948 and accounted from 2,800 of over 4,400 Centurions built.

13 marks of Centurion—the final versions equipped with the L7 105mm gun—proved themselves in action in all the Cold War hotspots from Korea onward for some 20 countries

| SPECIFICATION | |
|---|---|
| **Variant: Mk 3** | **Armour: 152mm (6in) max** |
| **Crew: 4** | **Engine: Rolls-Royce Meteor V12 petrol** |
| **Entered service: 1948** | **developing 650hp with a top speed** |
| **Weight: 49,786kg (49 tons)** | **of 35.4kph (22mph)** |
| **Dimensions:** | **Range: 192km (120 miles)** |
| **Length: 9.83m (32ft 3in)** | **Armament:** |
| **Height: 3m (9ft 10in)** | **Main: 1 x 20pdr** |
| **Width: 3.4m (11ft 2in)** | **Secondary: 1 x 7.92mm Besa MG** |

# A41 CENTURION

A 1st Royal Tank Regiment Centurion during Exercise Mailed Fist in 1969. The Centurion served from 1945 to the late 1960s.

The final version of the Centurion, the Mark 13, was equipped with the 105mm L7A2 gun. It also had an infrared searchlight and driving lights.

from Australia to Sweden, and Centurion Mk 5 AVREs were still in service with the British Army during the First Gulf War. Testament to its versatility was its protracted service with the Israeli Defence Force that carried on from the Six-Day War till the 1990s.

# T-54/T-55

## Medium Tank | USSR | 1947

Another design that appeared as WWII ended, the T-54/55 series was one of the largest ever produced: at least 60,000 and some sources quote 100,000. The first prototype appeared in March 1945 but full production only started in 1947 after many modifications including thicker hull armour. Quality control issues reduced output at first, but it quicly became the mainstay of postwar Eastern Bloc tank forces, including their satellites and 'clients' worldwide for at least 20 years. It was also built under licence in Czechoslovakia, Poland and China, and remained in production until the early 1990s.

The T-54 had a low silhouette and a classic mushroom dome turret, new models featuring many improvements such as night vision equipment, an extra machine gun for AA defence, upgrade programmes of fire control, navigation, communication and safety systems, as well as add-on armour. There were also endless variants. The T-54 was used in the invasion of Hungary in 1956.

### SPECIFICATION

Variant: **T-55**
Crew: **4**
Entered service: **1955**
Weight: **36,000kg (35.4 tons)**
Dimensions:
Length: **6.45m (21ft 2in)**
Height: **2.4m (7ft 10.5in)**
Width: **3.27m (10ft 8.5in)**
Armour: **203mm (8in) max**

Engine: **V-54 12-cylinder diesel developing 520hp with a top speed of 48kph (30mph)**
Range: **400km (250 miles)**
Armament:
Main: **1 x D-10T 100mm (3.9in) gun**
Secondary: **1 x SGMT 7.62mm (0.3in) coaxial and 1 x DShK 12.7mm (0.50in) AA MGs**

Ex-Polish T-54A at the Panzermuseum Thun in Switzerland.

Probably the most widely used tank ever—some estimates put total built at 100,000, often under licence. These are Polish T-54As on exercise.

The advent of T-55 in the 1950s tackled the main flaw—its automotive unreliability—by fitting a larger, water-cooled, diesel engine. There was also a new mushroom turret, without the loader's cupola or the prominent rooftop ventilator dome. Improved models surfaced regularly, sporting an array of enhancements and variants, including NBC protection, add-on armour suites, main gun stabilisation and fire control systems. While certainly lighter and smaller than the British Centurion or US Pattons, it was more than a match for them until outgunned by the L7 or M68 105mm. Often quoted is the experience of the Iran–Iraq war when Iranian Chieftains and M60s were trounced by Iraqi T-54s and T-62s—although tactics and training had a strong bearing on the outcome.

Variants included the ZSU-57-2 SPAAG, with two 57mm autocannon, which shot down RAF Tornados in the first Gulf War; an ARV, bridgelayer, CEV, flamethrower; the BTR-T APC; and SP guns including the SU-122-54 SP 122mm gun.

# M47, M48
## and **M60 Patton**

## Main Battle Tank | USA | 1952

**T**he M47 was derived from the M46, itself an M26 upgrade. Rushed into production during the Korean crisis, the M47 was cobbled together by adding a T42 turret onto an M46 body. The result, however, proved to be a durable design and after the teething problems it went on to have a distinguished and long

service life seeing combat for the Pakistani Army in 1965 when some 300 M47s did not show up well against the Indian Army's Centurions and in the Arab-Israeli conflicts where it was used more effectively by both Israel and Jordan.

The M47 sold well in the export market, putting in long years of service for a number of armies. Around 9,000 were built and major customers included Belgium (784), France (856), Greece (396), Iran (400), Italy (2,480), South Korea (531), Spain (389), Turkey (1,347) and West Germany (1,120).

In 1950, while the Korean War was still being waged, Chrysler was given a contract to build the follow-up M48, which

## SPECIFICATION

**Variant: M47**
**Crew: 5**
**Entered service: 1952**
**Weight: 48.000kg (48.6 tons)**
**Dimensions:**
**Length: 8.51m (27ft 11in)**
**Height: 3.35m (11ft)**
**Width: 3.51m (11ft 6in)**
**Armour: 4 in (100 mm)**

**Engine: Continental AV-1790-5B V12, air-cooled, Twin-turbo gasoline engine producing 810hp with a top speed of 60kph (37 mph)**
**Range: 160km (100 miles)**
**Armament:**
**Main: 90 mm gun**
**Secondary: 2 × 12.7 mm M2 machine guns and x1 7.62mm machine gun**

The Patton series started when M26 Pershing tanks were upgraded to M46/M46A1 standard.
The M47 (seen here) followed on and was the only Patton not to see action in US service.

was standardised just as the war for which it had been built ended. The new Patton, christened by the general's wife in July 1952, had some major improvements over the M47—it weighed less and was shorter—but it also had some major defects: the already poor range and fuel capacity, bad on the M47, was worse on the M48, as were the transmission, engine and running gear. These were improved incrementally on the M48A1, A2 and A3, the latter sporting a diesel engine with improved running gear. The M48A3 was the most numerous US tank in Vietnam and saw action in the Indo-Pakistan and Arab-Israeli conflicts.

The main visual differences between the M47 and M48 were the turret, which was more rounded than the M47's, and the loss of the hull machine gunner, the first US postwar tank to do so. The main weapon—the M41

90mm—was little better than the M47's but a larger turret ring allowed it to be upgraded, as it was in the mid-1970s to 105mm when the M48A5 was a major rebuild.

One of the first tanks to have an analogue mechanical fire control system, the M48 was also very popular on the export market selling in large quantities. It proved long-lived and of the nearly 11,700 M48 gun tanks built 1952–59 many served well into the new millennium. In the mid-1990s, upgraded to M48A5 standard the tank was in service with Greece (over 900), Israel (325), South Korea (850), Morocco (224), Pakistan (280), Spain (164), Taiwan (550) and Turkey (3,000). Some of the Korean and Turkish versions are still in service today.

The M60 was a natural progression and even more successful than the M47 and M48, with over 15,000 built, serving with over 20 countries.

## SPECIFICATION

**Variant: M48**
**Crew: 4**
**Entered service: 1953**
**Weight: 45,010kg (44.3 tons)**
**Dimensions:**
**Length: 9.31m (30ft 6.5in)**
**Height: 3.1m (10ft 2in**
**Width: 3.63m (11ft 11in)**
**Armour: 120mm (4.7in) max**

**Engine: Continental AVSI 1790-6**
**12-cylinder diesel developing 810hp**
**with a top speed of 48kph (30mph)**
**Range: 499km (310 miles)**
**Armament:**
**Main: 1 x 90mm T54 gun**
**Secondary: 1 x M73 7.62mm MG,**
**1 x Browning M2 0.50in AA MG**

Israeli M60s during the Yom Kippur War.

1st Marine Division M48 in Vietnam, April 1968.

# M47, M48 AND M60 PATTON

US Army soldiers load an M60 Patton onto a tank transporter at the National Guard Armory in Bluffton, IN, 30 June 2009.

Apart from the M60A2 armed with the 152mm gun/Shillelagh missile system, which proved a disappointment, the M60 had an excellent record. Regular upgrades improved armour, engines, guns and fire control systems, ammunition etc and kept the M60 in the front-line forces of many NATO countries. Of particular note are the Israeli Magach 6 and 7 versions (1–5 were based on the M48) improved with new tracks, fire control, smoke dischargers and ERA. The M60 may have been phased out of the US inventory, but the Israeli, Egyptian and Turkish tanks will stay in service for some years to come.

All three Pattons proved suitable chassis for variants with a number of mineclearers, CEVs, ARVs and AVLBs. The US M728 CEV and M60AVLB (both based on the M60) are still in service.

## SPECIFICATION

**Variant: M60**
**Crew: 4**
**Entered service: 1961**
**Weight: 46,026kg (45.3 tons)**
**Dimensions:**
**Length: 6.95m (22ft 9.5in)**
**Height: 3.13m (10ft 6.5in)**
**Width: 3.63m (11ft 11in)**

**Armour: 156mm (6.2in) max**
**Engine: AVDS 17902A V12 diesel developing 750hp with a top speed of 48kph (30mph)**
**Range: 482km (300 miles)**
**Armament:**
**Main: 1 x 105mm M68 gun**
**Secondary: 1 x 12.7 mm M73 machine gun**

M60A3s at the 1983 Canadian Army Trophy

The M60 was the mainstay of US forces during the Cold War when NATO tanks exercised regularly in Germany. This M60A1 of 8th Infantry Division negotiates a German village during Exercise Reforger 82.

# M41 Walker Bulldog

## Light Tank | USA | 1953

**W**ork started on an M24 replacement after the war, the first prototype designated T37 was built in 1949 and production started in 1951. Originally named the Little Bulldog, this was changed after the death of American hero General 'Johnnie' Walker in a traffic accident in Korea. The general had seen action in the Vera Cruz operation as well as WWI and WWII:

the light tank named after him also showed durability and longevity, remaining in service into the new millennium.

Tested in Korea, it took over the reconnaissance role from the US Army's M24s in 1953 and proved itself to be agile, with a good engine and main armament once the rangefinder had been improved. Its main deficiencies were the internal space—cramped for Americans this proved no obstacle to the South Vietnamese whose ageing M24s were replaced with M41s. The Walker Bulldog was heavy, too, meaning its airportability was a problem, and it was noisy—but its Continental six-cylinder engine was excellent and was improved with fuel injection (on the M41A1) and

---

### SPECIFICATION

| | |
|---|---|
| **Crew: 4** | **Engine: Continental AOS 895-3 6-cylinder diesel developing 500hp with a top speed of 72kph (45mph)** |
| **Entered service: 1953** | |
| **Weight: 21,319kg (21 tons)** | |
| **Dimensions:** | **Range: 160km (100 miles)** |
| **Length: 9.31m (19ft 1in)** | **Armament:** |
| **Height: 2.71m (8ft 9in)** | **Main: 1 x 76mm M32 gun** |
| **Width: 3.32m (10ft 6in)** | **Secondary: 1 x Browning 0.50in and** |
| **Armour: 38mm (1.5in) max** | **1 x Browning M1919 0.30in MGs** |

The M41 Walker Bulldog proved to be long-serving—over 6,000 had been produced by the time production ceased in the 1960s. This M41/B has been fitted with a Cockerill 90mm gun.

supercharging (M41A2 and A3) to give 500hp and a top speed of 72kph (45mph).

It was a great export seller, with major exports to Brazil (300), Spain (180), Taiwan (675) and Thailand (200). Upgrades included the 1997 NAPCO International of USA programme which created the M41D for Taiwan. It included sideskirts to reduce dust, banks of 6 x electrically operated smoke grenade dischargers on either side of the turret, new APFSDS-T ammunition and a US Detroit Diesel 8V-71T engine improving performance of the tank greatly. The upgrade increased weight to 25,000kg (24.5 tons).

# AMX 13

## Light Tank | France | 1954

**D**esigned just after WWII, the AMX 13 was a strikingly original vehicle that proved the stability of the design through its longevity and its worth in combat at Suez in the hands of both the French and Israelis, in the Six-Day War and with the Indians in the 1965 war against Pakistan. It started production in 1950, its name reflecting its original weight, and went on to serve with 25 countries, production ceasing in 1987 after some 7,700 had been built. Atelier de Construction Roanne was the primary contractor; from the early 1960s Mecanique Creusot-Loire took over; final vehicles were produce by GIAT in the late 1980s. The French took the bulk (4,300) with some 3,500 exported to countries as diverse as the Netherlands and Venezuela. The AMX 13 underwent a number of improvements over the years and spawned a family of successful variants. Its most distinctive feature was the oscillating turret that contained a fixed weapon—initially a long-barrelled 75mm self-loading main gun, later upgraded up to 90mm and finally in 1987, to a 105mm low-recoil gun. There

### SPECIFICATION

**Crew: 3**
**Entered service: 1953**
**Weight: 15,000kg (14.8 tons)**
**Dimensions:**
**Length: 4.88m (16ft)**
**Height: 2.3m (7ft 6.5in)**
**Width: 2.51m (8ft 3in)**
**Armour: 25mm (1in) max**

**Engine: SOFAM 8-cylinder petrol developing 250hp with a top speed of 60kph (37.3mph)**
**Range: 400km (250 miles)**
**Armament:**
**Main: 1 x 75mm (or 90mm or 105mm) gun**
**Secondary: 2 x 7.62mm MGs**

The AMX-13 was not built for night fighting, but some armies have fitted an infrared searchlight to the rear of the gunner's position and an infrared sight for the gunner.

were also changes of engine from petrol to diesel.

The main variants were: the *Char-Lance* SS.11 which mounted four guided missiles on each side of the main armament (later versions mounted HOT); the AMX 13/105 Modèle 58 for Argentina and the Netherlands sporting an FL-12 turret and 105mm main gun; the DCA 30 which mounted AA weapons; the PDP bridge-layer and Modèle 55 ARV. The chassis was also used to mount self-propelled guns.

# T-62

## Main Battle Tank | USSR | 1961

The T-62 was a development of the T-54/T-55 series, with an enlarged hull to take a new, centrally placed turret and larger main gun, the 115mm U5-TS smoothbore. This has distinct pros and cons: pros are that the smoothbores are lighter, cheaper and have a better MV than rifled weapons; cons are that they are less accurate. The T-62 became the primary MBT of the Soviet amoured forces during the 1970s. It also had an automatic shell ejector system, which worked from the recoil, ejecting the spent shell casings through a port in the rear of the turret. As with many MBTs of the period, a gunner's IR searchlight was mounted on the right, above the main gun. Later models included the usual improvements—gun stabilisation and fire control, NBC, communication and safety systems, add-on armour, and increased belly-armour for mine protection.

Although there were many variations on the T-54/55 chassis there were surprisingly few on the T-62, although the

### SPECIFICATION

**Crew: 4**
**Entered service: 1961**
**Weight: 40,000kg (39.4 tons)**
**Dimensions:**
**Length: 6.63m (21ft 9in)**
**Height: 2.39m (7ft 10in)**
**Width: 3.3m (10ft 10in)**
**Armour: 242mm (9.5in) max after 1972**

**Engine: V55 12-cylinder diesel developing 580hp with a top speed of 50kph (31mph)**
**Range: 450km (280 miles)**
**Armament:**
**Main: 1 x U-5TS 115mm gun**
**Secondary: 1 x PKT 7.62mm (0.30in) coaxial and 1 x DShK 12.7mm (0.50in) AA MGs**

T-62 main battle tank on parade. It was nowhere near as successful as the T-54/55, partly because of cost and partly because improved ammunition increased the power of the earlier tank.

gun tank (over 20,000 built) was upgraded regularly. The most recent T-62 modifications included the 9M116 Sheksna (AT-10/12 'Stabber') laser-beam-riding missile system which sees a 28kg missile fired from the main gun; the Volna fire-control system; ERA and side skirts; a modernised suspension system; and the V-55U engine.

It's difficult to identify how many T-62s are still in service: conservative estimates are 8,000, among some 18 Eastern Bloc countries in Asia, the Middle and Far East. North Korea has the biggest holding (1,800) after Russia. Other T-62s were produced by the Czechs and North Koreans.

Rear view of a T-62. Notice the two optional 200 litre drum-type fuel tanks.

T-62 laying a smokescreen. The Russian tanks of the 1950s and 1960s could produce a useful smokescreen by injecting vaporized diesel fuel into the exhaust system.

# Leopard 1

## Main Battle Tank | Germany | 1965

The Leopard 1 was one of the most widely used tanks in the West, in the 1970s and 1980s. It originated from an earlier development project shared by Germany, France and Italy. First rolled out on 9 September 1965, it was manufactured by Krauss-Maffei of Munich, the first tank built in Germany since WWII. The design concept emphasised firepower and mobility, so the armour was initially light, although it was increased in later marks. As main armament the Germans chose the excellent British-made L7 105mm rifled gun fitted with a gyroscopic stabiliser for accurate firing on the move. The engine was a reliable 830hp MTU diesel, which gave high acceleration and low fuel consumption. The tank was also fitted with automatic fire control, NBC protection and night vision equipment.

Its commercial success was considerable: 6,485 Leopard 1 gun tanks were built and 1,771 utility and AA variants. They sold to Belgium (334 1A5s ordered in 1968, since sold to Brazil), the Netherlands (468 ordered 1968–70 since sold to Chile who sold

## SPECIFICATION

Crew: **4**

Entered service: **1965**

Weight: **40,400kg (39.76 tons)**

Dimensions:

Length: **9.54m (31ft 3.5in)**

Height: **2.76m (9ft 0.5in)**

Width: **3.41m (11ft 2.5in)**

Armour: **70mm (2.75in) max**

Engine: **MTU MB 828 M500 multi-fuel developing 830hp with a top speed of 65kph (40.4mph)**

Range: **600km (373 miles)**

Armament:

Main: **1 x 105mm rifled gun**

Secondary: **2 x 7.62mm MGs**

LEOPARD 1

some to Ecuador), Norway (172 1As which saw 42 years in service from 1970), Italy (200 from Germany in 1971–72 and then 400 built under licence), Denmark (230 1A5DKs in 1976), Australia (90 1A3s in 1976), Canada (114 Cs in 1978), Turkey (300 delivered in 1982–83 and 1990–91) and Greece (103 1A3s in 1981; additionally over 400 bought from the Netherlands and Germany). Germany itself received 2,437.

The Leopard saw many improvements and changes during its life with improved armour and upgrading of fire control and optical systems. There were a number of important variants, particularly the Bergepanzer 2 ARV, the *Dachs* (Badger) AEV, the *Biber* (Beaver) AVLB and

the Flakpanzer Gepard armed with two 35mm cannon usable in both AA and anti-tank roles.

A searchlight is mounted over the main armament of this Leopard 1A1.

# M551 Sheridan

## Light Tank | USA | 1966

The unusual Sheridan was conceived to cover two roles: armoured reconnaissance and airborne fire support. This meant it had to be air-portable, speedy but with a powerful weapon—and with the arrival of the PT-76 in the Warsaw inventory, it had to be amphibious. As might be expected with all these roles, the result wasn't very successful. Production started in July 1966 and the first of 1,662 entered service in 1968 and it quickly became evident that the innovative main armament—the MGM-51 Shillelagh tube-launched wire-guided missile system, which could also fire 152mm conventional ammunition—was problematic. However, in combat the Shillelagh did have one advantage: the devastating 'beehive' round that contained 10,000 flechettes.

The aluminium chassis and steel turret combination ensured the Sheridan was light and, therefore, could negotiate paddyfields and streams that other US armoured vehicles could not. It had excellent fuel efficiency and range and an easy-riding

---

### SPECIFICATION

**Crew: 4**
**Entered service: 1969**
**Weight: 15.830kg (15.6 ton)**
**Dimensions:**
**Length: 6.30m (20ft 8in)**
**Height: 2.95m (9ft 8in)**
**Width: 2.82m (9ft 3in)**
**Armour: aluminium hull**

**Engine: Detroit Diesel 6V53T 6-cylinder diesel developing 300hp with a top speed of 43mph (70kph)**
**Range: 560km (348 miles)**
**Armament:**
**Main: 1 x M81E1 152mm gun/missile system**
**Secondary: 1 x M2 0.50in and 1 x 7.62mm M73 (later M219) MGs**

## M551 SHERIDAN

Spot the M551. This Sheridan has been visually modified to represent an opposing forces (OPFOR) tank, T-80, during battle exercises for the 177th Armored Brigade at the National Training Center, Fort Irwin, 1993.

...nd Airborne Division, driving an OPFOR M551 during training, 1996.

suspension and track system. Using a flotation screen, it could swim, but it was extremely vulnerable to many weapons, particularly by RPGs and mines: in *Vietnam Tracks* Simon Dunstan recounts the loss in a single day of five Sheridans from the 11th ACR to RPG fire. It was also not just air-portable but could be air-dropped using a low-velocity airdrop from a C-130, C-141 or C-5.

In spite of its defects, Sheridans continued in service with the 82nd Airborne Division until the 1990s, seeing service in the first Gulf War.

# FV4201 Chieftain

## Main Battle Tank | United Kingdom | 1963

The successor to Centurion started life in 1956, when Leyland Motors built three prototypes. Six more followed in 1961–62, leading to the Mk 1, 40 of which were built for use in field trials and training with 1st and 5th RTR. Initially troubles with the L60 engine blighted what was a significant improvement on the Centurion, but successive engine improvements finally produced a fine fighting machine that would have been bought by the IDF had it not been for political objections from other Middle Eastern countries. Over 1,350 Chieftains were eventually produced in 12 marks and it served with the British Army until 1996, the 450 export examples continuing in service into the 21st century.

The Chieftain had an impressively low silhouette thanks to the driver's reclining position, sloped glacis armour that gave good protection, the best gun in the world at the time—the 120mm L11A5 rifled tank gun, which used bagged charge,

| SPECIFICATION | |
|---|---|
| Variant: **Mk 5** | Width: **3.66m (12ft) including searchlight** |
| Crew: **4** | Armour: **Still classified** |
| Entered service: **Mk 1 1963;** **Mk 5 1970s** | Engine: **Leyland L60 petrol developing 720bhp with a top speed of 48kph (30mph)** |
| Weight: **55,000kg (54 tons) combat loaded** | Range: **400-500km (250-300 miles)** |
| Dimensions: | Armament: |
| Length: **10.87m (35ft 8in) gun forward** | Main: **120mm L11A7 rifled gun** |
| Height: **2.89m (9ft 6in)** | Secondary: **2 x 7.62mm MGs, one coaxial, one on commander's cupola** |

Chieftain of the Queen's Royal Irish Hussars, then based at Bhurtpore Barracks in Tidworth as the UKLF (reserve) tank regiment, arrives at Southampton Docks as part of Reforger 1979.

modern APFSDS ammunition and initially a .50cal Browning Ranging Machine—NBC equipment in the turret and snorkel wading equipment. The RMG was replaced by a laser sight and, subsequently, the fully integrated Marconi Improved Fire Control System. Added to this, gunnery was continuously improved by night IR/WL sights that were used in conjunction with the IR/WL searchlight mounted on the left hand side of the turret and a Thermal Observation and Gunnery Sight. The final upgrades incorporated a passive armour package known as 'Stillbrew'. There were three variants, an Armoured Repair and Recovery Vehicle, an AVRE and a bridgelayer.

# Stridsvagn Strv 103 S-Tank

## Main Battle Tank | Sweden | 1968

The radical Swedish Strv 103 or S-Tank was the first tank—as opposed to tank destroyer—expressly designed not to have a turret. This approach conferred both advantages and disadvantages to this most specific vehicle. Its incredibly low silhouette rendered the Strv 103 very difficult to spot at all when in its hull-down position and its dozer blade enabled it to virtually bury itself. Its main gun was fixed in its mounting, eliminating the need for a heavy mantlet but making the vehicle incapable of any traversing lateral movement without moving position by engaging its tracks. Elevation was obtained through adjustment of the hull suspension.

Because it could not fire on the move the driver became the gunner served by an autoloader. Both the commander and the driver/gunner had separate discrete fire control systems, with the commander able to override the latter's at any time. The third crew member was the radio operator, who was seated backwards behind

### SPECIFICATION

| | |
|---|---|
| **Variant: Strv 103B** | **Engine: Rolls-Royce K60 diesel developing 240hp and a Caterpillar 553 gas turbine developing 490hp with a top speed of 50kph (31mph)** |
| **Crew: 3** | |
| **Entered service: 1968** | |
| **Weight: 39.727kg (39 tons)** | |
| **Dimensions:** | **Range: 390km (240 miles)** |
| **Length: 9m (29ft 6in)** | **Armament:** |
| **Height: 2.5m (8ft 2.5in)** | **Main: Bofors 105 mm L/62 rifled gun** |
| **Width: 3.6m (11ft 10in)** | **Secondary: 2 x fixed and** |
| **Armour: 100mm (4in) max** | **1 x AA 7.62 mm KSP 58 MGs** |

Strv 103 was armed with a Bofors 105mm L/62 that was attached to the hull, and therefore could not be stabilised - and so could only fire when stationary.

the driver and also had controls for driving the vehicle backwards. The S-Tank was also the first tank to use a turbine engine, and was

unusual Strv 103 S-tank retired in 1997. Note the anti-HEAT grille.

designed and manufactured in the 1950s as a primarily defensive AFV with a specific terrain in mind—the Swedish fields and tundra exposed to low temperatures with much snow and rain.

Some 300 S-tanks were built in three versions—the 103A was the initial model; the 103B had a dozer blade and integral flotation screen; the 103C was a major upgrade in 1986 that added life to the A and B versions, taking the S-tanks' use into the 1990s until replaced by the Strv 122, the Swedish version of the Leopard 2. Upgrade programmes including add-on armour suites, ingenious sideskirts that incorporated extra fuel cells, and a new Detroit Diesel 290hp diesel engine.

# Combat Vehicle Reconnaissance

## Tracked vehicles | United Kingdom | 1972

### SPECIFICATION

| | |
|---|---|
| Variant: **Scorpion** | Armour: **Classified** |
| Crew: **3** | Engine: **Jaguar 4.2-litre petrol** |
| Entered service: **1973** | **developing 190hp with a top** |
| Weight: **7,800kg (7.67 tons)** | **speed of 80.5kph (50mph)** |
| Dimensions: | Range: **644km (400 miles)** |
| Length: **4.39m (14ft 5in)** | Armament: |
| Height: **2.08m (6ft 10in)** | Main: **1 x 76mm or 90mm gun** |
| Width: **2.18m (7ft 2in)** | Secondary: **1 x 7.62mm coaxial MG** |

| | |
|---|---|
| Variant: **Scimitar** | Armour: **Classified** |
| Crew: **3** | Engine: **Jaguar 4.2-litre petrol** |
| Entered service: **1973** | **developing 190hp with a top** |
| Weight: **78.000kg (7.67 tons)** | **speed of 80.5kph (50mph)** |
| Dimensions: | Range: **644km (400 miles)** |
| Length: **4.38m (14ft 5in)** | Armament: |
| Height: **2.09m (6ft 10in)** | Main: **1 x 30mm Rarden cannon** |
| Width: **2.18m (7ft 2in)** | Secondary: **1 x 7.62mm MG** |

Designed in the 1960s to replace the Saladin wheeled armoured car and Saracen APC, Alvis's CVR(T) family comprised: Scorpion (fire support), Scimitar (light recce), Spartan (APC), Samson (recovery) Striker (anti-tank guided weapon) later replaced by Stormer, Sultan (command vehicle) and Samaritan (ambulance). They had to be air-portable so they had to be small and light: aluminium armour was the solution and this kept Scorpion's weight to under 8,000kg (just under 8 tons) although improved performance packages have seen this creep up to some 12,000kg (under 12 tons). In turn their size and weight ensured a fast top speed (80kph/50mph).

Wintry training for Scimitar crews—the vehicle saw action in the Falklands, the first Gulf War and Afghanistan.

Alvis won an MoD contract in 1967 and in January 1972 the British Army took delivery of its first production vehicles. Total production for the British Army was 313 Scorpions, 89 Strikers, 691 Spartans, 50 Samaritans, 291 Sultans, 95 Samsons and 334 Scimitars. The family was an export success and sold to a number of countries, 3,500 units in all were produced, of which 1,863 went to the MoD and around 700 were delivered to Belgium in 1975. While Belgium and other European countries disposed of their CVR(T)s by 2004, successful deployment in the Falklands War, two Gulf Wars, in the Balkans and latterly service in Afghanistan led to the British Army to keep some CVR(T)s through a number of improvement programmes culminating in

2011 when the CVR(T) Mk 2 next generation variants of Scimitar, Spartan, Sultan, Samaritan and Samson entered service in Afghanistan.

1,500 Scorpions served with the British armed forces from 1974 to 1994 .

# T-72

## Main Battle Tank | USSR | 1973

**D**uring the 1960s it became apparent to the Soviets that NATO was gaining an advantage with new anti-tank weapons and sophisticated laminate armour, leaving the T-54/55/62 series anachronistic. This led to the development of two distinct lines: the T-64, an expensive, highly complicated tank with innovative laminate armour, a new gun equipped with an autoloader and an advanced powerpack and suspension. This vehicle was right at the top of the tree when it was produced and became the mainstay of Russian tank units; 8,000 were produced and were not provided to USSR's allies to ensure the advanced technology did not fall into the wrong hands. Its main drawbacks were cost and a problematic powerpack.

The other development was the T-72, which had a classic Russian low rounded turret centred on the hull with cupolas for commander and loader and a crew of three. (The turret was, in fact, so low was the T-72 that the rumour started that only midgets could crew it.) The original

| SPECIFICATION | |
|---|---|
| **Variant: T-72A** | **Engine: V46 12-cylinder diesel developing 780hp with a top speed of 60ph (37mph)** |
| **Crew: 3** | |
| **Entered service: 1973** | |
| **Weight: 41,460kg (40.8 tons)** | **Range: 460km (290 miles); greater with fuel drums** |
| **Dimensions:** | |
| **Length: 9.53m (31ft 3in)** | **Armament:** |
| **Height: 2.22m (7ft 3in)** | **Main: 1 x 125mm 2A46M smoothbore gun** |
| **Width: 3.59m (12ft 9in)** | |
| **Armour: 250mm (9.8in) max** | **Secondary: 1 x 7.62mm (0.30** |

armament was a 125mm D-81TM smoothbore tank subsequently upgraded and replaced by a 125mm 2A46 smoothbore gun. In 1985 the T-72B entered service. A great improvement on the initial version, it had a new 2A46M main gun capable of firing the 9M119 Svir (AT-11 'Sniper') guided missile, better fire control system, additional armour and an improved a new V-84-1 840hp engine. The T-72BM was introduced in 1992 and improved under the 'Rogatka' programme with a new 125mm 2A46M-5 main,

An Iraqi T-72 tank during a firing exercise with US troops assigned to the 3rd Battalion, 69th Armor Regiment and Ninth Iraqi Army, Besmaya range, Iraq, 14 April 2010.

V-92S2 1,000hp diesel engine and new Relikt third-generation ERA which is claimed to be twice as effective as Kontakt-5.

Lightweight in spite of its thick cast armour, with a comprehensive NBC system, the T-72 was built in massive numbers—over 25,000—and supplied to over 40 'client' and satellite states. It was also built under licence by seven other countries including Czechoslovakia, Poland and Yugoslavia.

T-72s have seen combat in most of the conflicts of the last 35 years from the Iran-Iraq war where they performed well against the Iranian M60s and Chieftains—to the two Gulf Wars when they were cut to pieces by US Abrams and British Challengers.

...iers with the Iraqi Army's 9th Division check their T-72 before driving to ...ing range at Forward Operating Base Hammer in Iraq 31 October 2008.

# Type 74 Nana-yon

## Main Battle Tank | Japan | 1975

After WWII the Japanese were demilitarised and all military manufacturing ceased. However, the advent of the Korean War and the proliferation of ideological friction between the Communist and Western powers meant that Japan needed to be rearmed. The US supplied tanks of WWII vintage and subsequently in the mid-1950s what became the JGSDF needed to decide between buying American M47s and manufacturing their own vehicle. The Type 61 was the result, a 35-ton tank armed with a 90mm gun and powered by a Mitsubishi 12HM21WT 12-cylinder diesel engine of 570hp giving a road speed of 45kph (28mph). 560 were built by Mitsubishi 1961–75 before it was replaced by the Type 74.

The Type 74, designed in 1962–64 by Mitsubishi Heavy Industries, to be comparable to the Leopard 1 or M60 took some years to reach production, which started in September 1975. When production ceased in 1989 893 tanks had been produced.

| SPECIFICATION | |
|---|---|
| **Variant: Type 74** | **Engine: Mitsubishi 10ZF22WT** |
| **Crew: 4** | **10-cylinder diesel developing** |
| **Entered service: 1975** | **720hp with a top speed of** |
| **Weight: 38,000kg (37.4 tons)** | **60kph (38mph)** |
| **Dimensions:** | **Range: 400km (250 miles)** |
| **Length: 9.42m (30ft 10in)** | **Armament:** |
| **Height: 2.48m (8ft 2in)** | **Main: 1 x 105mm L7 gun** |
| **Width: 3.18m (10ft 5in)** | **Secondary: 1 x 7.62mm and** |
| **Armour: Unspecified** | **1 x 12.7mm MGs** |

A Type 74 of the Japanese Ground Self Defense Force (JGSDF) during an open day in Itami-city, Hyogo, Japan. Designed in the 1960s, when it was eventually entered service it was outdated.

The Type 74 was armed with the British 105mm L7 rifled tank gun, manufactured under licence in Japan, originally to be linked to an autoloader, but this was dropped due to costs. It was upgraded in service with IR imagers, a laser rangefinder for the commander, a new digital FCS for the gunner and improved ammunition. A 1993 upgrade package that added side skirts and a passive IR system was cancelled on cost grounds.

The Type 74 spawned a number of variants: the Type 87 SPAAG, Type 78 ARV and Type 91 AVLB.

A Type 74 tank on display at the JGSDF Ordnance School in Tsuchiura, Kanto, Japan.

# T-80

## Main Battle Tank | USSR | 1976

The T-80 was developed from the T-64 and entered service in 1976. Weighing 40 tons and fitted with torsion bar suspension, it was the first Soviet tank to have a gas-turbine engine, the GTD 1000, much to the surprise of Western commentators. While this improved on the T-64's powerpack, the gas turbine was greedy and over the years there have been many attempts to increase fuel stowage to compensate. The T-80B had a new turret, composite armour and an autoloader allowing the firing of 9M112-1 Kobra (AT-8 'Songster') anti-tank guided missile. It entered service in 1978, and was regularly improved with 1,100hp engine in 1980, a new gun in 1982. The T-80A of 1982 saw a larger and better-armoured turret being adopted for both this tank and the T-64BM. 1985 saw the arrival of the T-80U which had K5 ERA, the 9K119 Refleks

## SPECIFICATION

**Variant: T-80B**
**Crew: 3**
**Entered service: 1978**
**Weight: 42,500kg (41.83 tons)**
**Dimensions:**
**Length: 7.4m (24ft 3in)**
**Height: 2.2m (7ft 3in)**
**Width: 3.4m (11t 2in)**
**Armour: Unspecified**
**Engine: SG-1000 12-cylinder**

**gas turbine developing 1,100hp**
**with a top speed of 70kph (43mph)**
**Range: 335km (208 miles);**
**more with external tanks**
**Armament:**
**Main: 1 x 125mm 2A46-2**
**smoothbore gun**
**Secondary: 1 x 7.62mm (0.30in)**
**PKT coaxial and 1 x 12.7mm**
**(0.50in) NSVT MGs**

The T-80 MBT was the first Russian tank to use a gas-turbine engine. In 1993 Boris Yeltsin used tanks against the Supreme Soviet and T-80UD tanks fired on the Russian parliament.

(AT-11 'Sniper') missile system—which has a 5,000m (5,500yd) range—and in 1990 a new 1,250hp engine.

Some 4,500 T-80s are in service in Russia, plus a small number in other countries. The Ukraine builds a modified version, the T-84.

# M1 Abrams

## Main Battle Tank | USA | 1978

**P**robably the most formidable tank in the world, certainly the most carefully developed, the GDLS M1 Abrams has been the principal combat tank of the US Army since 1980. It has been regularly updated to ensure it maintains its pole position. As befits the world's top superpower, the Abrams uses state-of-the-art technology at every point. It was built using steel-encased depleted-uranium armour as protection against modern anti-tank weapons; its main weapon is the 120mm M256 smoothbore developed by Rheinmetall GmbH of Germany, firing a number of specialised rounds designed to combat enemy vehicles equipped with next-generation ERA; HEAT shaped-charge rounds; and anti-personnel canister.

The first M1 came into service in 1978. 3,273 were produced 1979–85 for the US Army. The M1A1 arrived in 1985—4,796 were built for the US Army, 221 for the US Marines and 880 co-produced with Egypt 1985–92. Only 77

| SPECIFICATION | |
|---|---|
| **Variant: M1A1** | **Engine: Honeywell AGT 1500C multi-fuel turbine developing 1,500hp with a top speed of 67kph (42mph)** |
| **Crew: 4** | |
| **Entered service: 1980** | |
| **Weight: 61,369kg (60.4 tons)** | **Range: 426km (265 miles)** |
| **Dimensions:** | **Armament:** |
| **Length: 9.77m (32ft 3in)** | **Main: 1 x 120mm L/44 M256 smoothbore** |
| **Height: 2.44m (8ft)** | |
| **Width: 3.66m (12ft)** | **Secondary: 2 x 7.62mm M240 and** |
| **Armour: Classified** | **1 x 0.50in Browning M2HB MGs** |

A US Army Abrams M1A1 tank takes a defensive position at a staging area during Exercise Ready Crucible in Germany, on 11 February 2005.

M1A2 tanks were built for the US Army, from 1992 (additionally, 315 for Saudi Arabia and 218 for Kuwait), but 600 M1s were upgraded to M1A2 configuration at the Lima Army tank plant 1996–2001. Currently the M1A2SEP (System Enhancement Package) is the most advanced standard variant. The US Army expects the M1A2 to be in service until 2050. The Abrams also has available a TUSK—Tank Urban Survival Kit—package to improve survivability in areas that tanks don't thrive. Also under development is the M1A3 due to enter service in 2017. In an attempt to reduce the weight—the M1A2 is over 7,100kg (7 tons) heavier than the M1 weighing in at 64,000kg

(63 tons)—the M1A3 will have a new lighter gun, improved suspension, lighter armour and hopes tio use fibre optic lines to reduce weight overall by 2,030kg (2 tons)

There are a number of specialised variants: the M1 Panther II remote-controlled mine-clearing vehicle, of which there are six in service; the M104 Wolverine heavy assault bridge (44 in service); and the M1ABV Assault Breacher Vehicle a number of which are in service with the USMC

The Abrams has been tested in combat and proved its effectiveness in two Gulf wars, where, together with Challenger, it dominated the battlefield with few casualties.

4,796 M1A1s have been produced for the US Army.

Live-firing training at Fort Hood, TX in 2013. The M1A2 Abrams' 120mm L/44 M256 smoothbore main gun is built under licence from Rheinmetall.

# Merkava

## Main Battle Tank | Israel | 1979

As one would expect from a country that has had so much experience in tank warfare, the Merkava (Chariot), Israel's first indigenous MBT, benefited from a clearcut identification of requirements and a practical if innovative design to achieve them. A small country, Israel has to put special emphasis on crew protection and much of the Merkava's design is about survivability, in particular the frontally located engine; careful use of active and spaced armour on the frontal arc; side skirts and track protectors; use of internal bulkheads and the rear doors to the hull that make bombing up easier to accomplish.

Work started on the Merkava when the joint British-Israeli Chieftain project ended politically in 1969. Design completed in 1974, and the prototype rolled off the production lines in 1977. Merkava first reached the IDF in 1979, the first of 250 built. Its main armament was the M68, a licensed copy of the British L7 105mm capable of firing the LAHAT ATGM. Baptism by fire

| SPECIFICATION | |
|---|---|
| Variant: **Mk I** | Armour: **Classified** |
| Crew: **4** | Engine: **Teledyne AVDS 12-cylinder** |
| Entered service: **1979** | **diesel developing 908hp, with a** |
| Weight: **62,000kg (61.02 tons)** | **top speed of 50kph (31mph)** |
| Dimensions: | Range: **500km (310 miles)** |
| Length: **7.45m (24ft 5in)** | Armament: |
| **without gun** | Main: **1 x 105mm gun** |
| Height: **2.65m (8ft 8in)** | Secondary: **3 x 7.62mm MGs;** |
| Width: **3.7m (12ft 2in)** | **1 x external 60mm mortar** |

was in the Lebanon in 1982 when 180 Merkavas spearheaded Israeli operations, proving themselves impervious to the anti-tank weapons used against them and much the better of the T-62s they fought.

However, there were lessons to be learnt—34 tanks were lost—and Merkava II benefited from them. It had increased engine performance, anti-rocket netting protection against infantry RPGs. and updates to optics and fire control as well as additional top armour. The 60mm mortar, external on the Mk I, was brought in side the vehicle. It entered service in 1983 and 580 were built 1982–89.

The Merkava III entered service 1989 sporting a new main gun, this time made

Merkava MkIII with a mine roller attached—one of the many anti-mine options that have been tried. Rollers and flails still seem the best bet.

the Israeli-made MG251 120mm smoothbore with a thermal sleeve to increase accuracy by preventing heat distortion. There was also a new suspension system, an improved 1,200hp engine and new transmission, and ballistic protection provided by further special add-on armour modules, although this would not stop some losses to mines in the Second Intifada of 2006. 780 Merkava IIIs were built 1990–2002.

In 2003 the Merkava IV started production, with a likely 660 to be built. It has further improved night and remote vision devices, a new MTU/General Dynamics 1,500hp diesel engine, an enhanced MG253 main gun and increased modular passive armour.

The most recent upgrade of the Merkava is the Mk IV which entered ce in 2004. This one is at the Yad La-Shiryon Museum, Latrin, Israel.

# Leopard 2

## Main Battle Tank | Germany | 1979

The Leopard 1 was phased out and replaced by Leopard 2 also built by Krauss-Maffei (now Krauss-Maffei Wegmann). Leopard 2 had also started in a shared project that failed, this time the MBT-70 between Germany and USA. The development of the Leopard 2 was based on the desire to improve the firepower and protection of the Leopard 1 without affecting its unrivalled agility. The result was rolled out on 25 October 1979, sporting a Rheinmetall 120mm smoothbore and powered by a 1,500hp MTU MB873 turbocharged diesel engine with an advanced torsion bar suspension system that made for an extremely good cross-country performance.

From the day the first of 3,480 Leopard 2s rolled off the production line, upgrading packages have ensured the Leopard 2 keeps abreast of technology and customer requirements. It has needed to. Many of those countries that bought Leopard 1 have bought Leopard 2. The first customer was the Netherlands (445 delivered 1981–86; 283

| SPECIFICATION | |
|---|---|
| **Variant: 2A5** | **Armour: Classified** |
| **Crew: 4** | **Engine: MTU MB 873 Ka501 12-cylinder diesel developing 1,500hp with a top speed of 72kph (45mph)** |
| **Entered service: 1995** | |
| **Weight: 62,500kg max (61.5 tons)** | |
| **Dimensions:** | **Range: 450km (280 miles)** |
| **Length: 9.97m (32ft 8.5in)** | **Armament:** |
| **Height: 2.64m (8ft 8in)** | **Main: 1 x 120mm Rheinmetall L55 smoothbore gun** |
| **Width: 3.77m (12ft 3in)** | **Secondary: 2 x 7.62mm MGs** |

subsequently sold to Austria, Canada, Norway and Portugal). Next came Sweden (280 of which 160 2A4s from Germany as the Stridsvagn 121, the others Leopard 2(S) models—Stridsvagn 122); Spain (108 2A4 models and 219 license-built Leopard 2A6); Switzerland (380 bought 1987–1993). Other users include Poland, Denmark, Finland, Greece (license-built as the Leopard 2Hel), Turkey and Chile. Germany has some 2,125 Leopard 2s in various versions.

The improvement packages have seen some significant alterations, including a change to the L44 and, later in the 2A6, L55 main armament. Armour protection changed visibly with the 2A5 when wedge-shaped paced armour was added to the turret altering the original vertical-sided look. Other changes included an electronic turret and weapons-driving mechanism, a commander's periscope equipped with its own IR camera/thermal imaging device, a modern navigation system and a reversing camera.

In combat the Leopard 2 has proved itself durable and efficient, seeing action in Kosovo with the German Army, Bosnia-Herzegovina with the Dutch and Afghanistan with the Danish and Canadian armies. There have been a number of IED incidents, in one of which a crew member died, but there have been good reports of the tank's ability to withstand explosions. As the *Grand Prairie Daily Herald Tribune* reported one Canadian officer saying in 2007,

German Leopard 2A5 training. Compare the turret shape to the 2A4 in the next photo. From the 2A5 on, Leopard 2 has added spaced armour on the turret.

'My crew stumbled upon an IED and made history as the first to test the [Leopard 2A6] M-packet. It worked as it should.'

Austrian Leopard 2A4 showing off the slabby vertical tungsten/titanium armour.

# Type 69/Type 79

## Main Battle Tank | China | 1982

The Type 69, followed by the Type 79, were the first domestically developed MBTs made by China, both tracing their lineage to the Type 59 which was a Chinese-built T-54A. The Type 59 was built in large numbers—nearly 10,000—and served well into the 2000s upgunned with the British L7 105mm.

The Type 69 programme began following the end of cooperation between China and the Soviet Union. The first Type 69 had many new domestically produced features including a new engine, and mounted a new 100mm main gun with new fire control systems, but it was rejected by the PLA, which was unhappy with its performance, particularly the smoothbore 100mm. After further improvements (some bought, others captured and copied) it was grudgingly accepted and though not used much by the PLA it sold well abroad. Customers included Pakistan, Bangladesh, Burma, Thailand, Sri Lanka, Zimbabwe and it was especially popular in the Middle East (Iran and

| SPECIFICATION | |
|---|---|
| **Variant: Type 69** | **Engine: 1210L-7BW 12-cylinder** |
| **Crew: 4** | **diesel developing 580hp with a** |
| **Entered service: 1983** | **top speed of 50kph (31mph)** |
| **Weight: 36,700kg (36.1 tons)** | **Range: 420km (261 miles)** |
| **Dimensions:** | **Armament:** |
| **Length: 6.24m (20ft 5.5in)** | **Main: 1 x 100mm gun** |
| **Height: 2.81m (9ft 2.5in)** | **Secondary: 2 x 7.62mm MGs** |
| **Width: 3.3m (10ft 10in)** | **and 1 x 12.7mm AA MG** |
| **Armour: 100mm (4in) max** | |

Iraq), where its robust simplicity was appreciated. The Type 69-II was armed with a rifled 100mm main gun and had improved fire control, an externally mounted laser rangefinder, and IR and night-fighting equipment.

In the 1980s, following a thaw in relations with the West, China had access to more advanced technologies and began the development of the Type 79, which entered production in the mid-1980s and featured a British internal laser rangefinder, an improved fire control system and a new 105mm L7 main gun.

Type 69s and 79s were used extensively by Iraq in the Gulf wars, often with appliqué armour and sideskirts, but apart from the occasional fixed position ambush they were no match for the US Abrams and British Challengers.

Variants of both vehicles include a command version with additional communications equipment, a turretless armoured recovery vehicle equipped with crane and dozer blade, and a civilian firefighting unit.

Chinese-built T-69 Type II MBT in front of Cox Hall, Quantico, VA, was dedicated to the enlisted Marines of The Basic School on 7 June 2000 during a memorial dedication for Sgt Manuel A. Cox who died 4 December 1983 as the result of the 1983 Marine Barracks bombing in Beirut.

The T-69 Type IIG Mk 2 entered Bangladeshi service in the 1980s with a 120mm main gun capable of firing ATGWs.

# Challenger

## Main Battle Tank | United Kingdom | 1983

The successful line of British MBTs that started with the Comet progressed to the new millennium with the Challenger 1. It was based on the Shir, an export version of the Chieftain designed from 1976 by the Military Vehicles and Engineering Establishment at Chobham to equip the Shah of Iran's armoured regiments. However, the Iranian Revolution in 1979 put paid to that deal and the British Army became the recipient of what proved to be an excellent stopgap between Chieftain and the Challenger 2—and one that saw more desert use than was perhaps envisaged in the late 1970s.

The British Army had identified a need to replace its ageing Chieftains and had been cooperating in a joint European venture, MBT-80. When this fell through, the availability of the Challenger 1 led in September 1978 to an MoD order for 243 from ROF Leeds. The first tanks being delivered to the Royal Hussars in April 1983, and further MoD orders

| SPECIFICATION | |
|---|---|
| Variant: **Challenger 1** | Engine: **Rolls-Royce CV12 diesel developing 1,200hp with a top speed of 57kph (35mph)** |
| Crew: **4** | |
| Entered service: **1982** | |
| Weight: **62,000kg (61.02 tons)** | Range: **450km (280 miles)** |
| Dimensions: | Armament: |
| Length: **8.33m (26ft 4in)** | Main: **1 x 120mm L11A5 gun** |
| Height: **2.5m (8ft 2.5in)** | Secondary: **2 x 7.62mm MGs, one coaxial, one on commander's cupola** |
| Width: **3.52m (11ft 6.5in)** | |
| Armour: **Classified** | |

Challenger 1s of British 1st Armoured Division during Operation Granby, the UK involvement in the first Gulf War.

brought the final total built to 420. It served with the British Army until around 2000 when it was superseded by the Challenger 2. The bulk of the British Army Challengers had a second life when, in March 1999, it was agreed that 288 would be supplied to Jordan—where it was renamed Al Hussein—with a new, unmanned turret.

The most obvious difference to Chieftain was Challenger's special ceramic composite 'Chobham' armour, which was developed to improve resistance to HEAT rounds and shatters KE projectiles. The new technology was shared with the Americans whose M1 Abrams uses the armour. Its main armament was the Royal Ordnance 120mm L11A5 rifled main gun, which more than proved its worth in the first Gulf War. Operation Granby, the British involvement in Operation Desert Storm, reported that Challengers destroyed some 300 Iraqi MBTs for no loss including a T-72 killed at over 5km (three miles), the longest

# CHALLENGER

A Challenger 2 of A Squadron, 1st Royal Tank Regiment -the world's oldest armoured regiment.

tank-on-tank kill in history. After its embarrassingly poor results at the 1987 Canadian Army Trophy competition, there had been some doubts about the Challenger whose automotive reliability was also questioned. The Gulf War dramatically dissipated these concerns. Of the 59 Challengers that attacked with 4th Armoured Brigade, 53 ended the battle intact after an advance of some 350km (220 miles)—and by the end of the war, thanks to the tireless work of the REME and Vickers, Challenger had a better serviceability record than the Abrams.

The replacement for Challenger 1 carries the same name and shares its predecessor's hull and automotive parts. It is, however, a very different beast that has been considerably improved, boasting second-generation Chobham armour (called Dorchester armour), a virtually new turret with the latest generation in digital computer technology, rangefinding, sighting, a state-of-the-art NBC suite and an improved Royal Ordnance L30 120mm rifled main gun with a coaxially mounted McDonnell Douglas Helicopter Systems 7.62mm chain gun. The main gun will be updated with a 120mm smoothbore gun capable of

## SPECIFICATION

**Variant: Challenger 2**
**Crew: 4**
**Entered service: 1992**
**Weight: 62,500kg (61.51 tons)**
**Dimensions:**
**Length: 8.327m (27ft 4in)**
**Height: 2.49m (8ft 2in)**
**Width: 3.52m (11ft 6in)**
**Armour: Classified**

**Engine: Perkins CV12 TCA Condor diesel developing 1,200hp with a top speed of 60kph (37mph)**
**Range: 450km (280 miles)**
**Armament:**
**Main: 1 x 120mm L30A1 gun**
**Secondary: 2 x 7.62mm MGs, one coaxial, one on commander's cupola**

firing standard NATO ammunition as part of the Challenger Lethality Improvement Programme. Developed privately by Vickers, the MoD ordered 386 Challenger 2s and 22 driver training tanks in two orders of June 1991 and 1994 valued at over £1.3 million after a competition that included the M1A2 Abrams and Leopard 2. Oman also ordered 38 Challenger 2s. Deliveries began in January 1998 to the Royal Scots Dragoon Guards in Germany. In 2003 16 Challenger 2s were deployed in the second Gulf War as 7th Armoured Brigade. They performed excellently with over 90 percent availability and the only loss being a tragic blue-on-blue engagement.

A Royal Scots Dragoon Guards Challenger during a training exercise in Basra, Iraq, 17 November 2008.

# T–90

## Main Battle Tank | Russia | 1991

**B**uilt by Uralvagonzavod in Nizhny Tagil—the largest MBT manufacturer in the world, this comprehensive upgrade of the T-72 incorporates many features from the T-80 alongside which it was developed. There are differences: the main one is the choice of powerpack, which for T-90 was an 840hp diesel engine. It has the classic Russian low, rounded turret centred on the hull. Its main armament is the 125mm 2A46 smoothbore main gun (as for T-72 and T-80). Distinctively, it has two infrared searchlights, one on either side of the main armament; they are part of its anti-missile defence system. The frontal of the turret is covered with second-generation reactive armour, making it one of the best protected of Russian MBTs. It also has the Shtora-1 defensive aids suite produced by Electronintorg of Russia. This includes an infrared jammer, laser warning system, grenade discharging system which produces an aerosol screen and a computerised control system. It is equipped with the latest, fire control, navigation and safety systems. Currently Russia has

### SPECIFICATION

**Crew: 3**
**Entered service: 1991**
**Weight: 47,500kg (46.7 tons)**
**Dimensions:**
**Length: 9.63m (31ft 7in)**
**Height: 2.22m (7ft 3in)**
**Width: 3.78m (12ft 5in)**
**Armour: Classified**

**Engine: V84MS 12-cylinder diesel developing 840hp with a top speed of 60kph (37mph)**
**Range: 550km (340 miles)**
**Armament:**
**Main: 1 x 125mm smoothbore gun**
**Secondary: 1 x 7.62mm (0.30in) PKMT and 1 x 12.7mm (0.50in) Kord MGs**

The T-90S is Indian Army's version of the Russian T-90. It's named 'Bhishma' after a Hindu warrior in the *Mahabharata*.

550 T-90As in service but from 2011, the Russian armed forces have ceased ordering the T-90, and are waiting for the T-99 expected to enter service in 2020.

The initial export version was the T-90S, since upgraded to T-90SM. An initial 310 were bought by the Indian Army in 2001— the order has since increased to over 600. Algeria has ordered 305 and Azerbaijan 94 with an option for another 94.

The T-90 has variants in the form of the BREM-72 ARV, MTU-90 bridgelayer, IMR-3 CEV and BMR-3 mineclearing vehicle.

The most modern tank in the Russian Army inventory, a T-90A on display during May 2013.

# Type 90 Kyu-maru

## Main Battle Tank | Russia | 1991

The Type 74 entered service in 1976 and the Type 90, its successor, went onto the drawing board at the same time. Prototypes were set in motion by Mitsubishi Heavy Industries and Japan Defense Agency's Technology Research and Development Institute and, armed with a 120mm Japan Steel Works gun, were completed by 1986. Further prototypes were produced and it was found cheaper to licence-build the Rheinmetall L44 120mm smoothbore main gun. Four more prototypes were produced using the German gun and eventually the Type 90 entered service in 1990.

It is a typical third-generation vehicle, similar to the Leopard 2, Leclerc and Chinese Type 96, its turret looking very like the Abrams. What is unusual is that the Rheinmetall gun is fed by an autoloader and so allows a reduction of the crew to three. Innovative technology includes laser and thermal-guided gun and turret controls. With a hybrid

| SPECIFICATION | |
|---|---|
| **Crew: 3** | **Engine: Mitsubishi 10ZG 10-cylinder** |
| **Entered service: 1991** | **diesel developing 1,500hp with a** |
| **Weight: 50,000kg (49.2 tons)** | **top speed of 70kph (43mph)** |
| **Dimensions:** | **Range: 400km (250 miles)** |
| **Length: 9.76m (32ft)** | **Armament:** |
| **Height: 2.34m (7ft 11in)** | **Main: 1 x 120mm gun** |
| **Width: 3.43m (11ft 4in)** | **Secondary: 1 x 7.62mm and** |
| **Armour: Unspecified** | **1 x 12.7mm MGs** |

GSDF Type 10 production model at the 1st Armored aining Unit/Eastern Army Combined Brigade, 2012.

hydropneumatic and torsion bar suspension system, composite and laminate armour, the Type 90 is powered by the Mitsubishi 10ZG ten-cylinder liquid-cooled diesel. There are three variants: an ARV, AVLB and mineclearer and a total of 341 tanks have been procured and delivered.

A Japanese Type 90 Main Battle Tank at the JGSDF Ordnance School in Tsuchiura, Kanto, Japan October 2007.

# AMX Leclerc

## Main Battle Tank | France | 1992

Named for the general who had spear-headed the drive for Paris in 1944, the Leclerc developed from a Franco-German tank design project of the 1980s, which would have been named Napoleon I in French service. Partnered instead by the UAE who ordered 436 (10 more than the French Army ordered) development took place by Giat Industries (now known as Nexter Systems) 1986–1990 when production started, the Leclerc entering service in 1992 to replace the French Army's ageing AMX 30s. While fewer vehicles than expected were produced—at one stage the French talked about the need for 1,400 vehicles—it is still the prime weapon of French armoured forces with some 250 upgraded vehicles in service.

With ceramic composite armour, a 120mm smoothbore weapon with an autoloader, a hydropneumatic suspension system, improved and mod-ernised electronics and thermal imaging systems, a digital fire control system which allows the

### SPECIFICATION

Crew: **3**

Entered service: **1992**

Weight: **56,000kg (55.1 tons)**

Dimensions:

Length: **9.87m (32ft 4.5in)**

Height: **2.53m (8ft 3.5in)**

Width: **3.71m (12ft 2in)**

Armour: **Classified**

Engine: **SACM V8X 12-cylinder diesel developing 1,500hp with a top speed of 72kph (45mph)**

Range: **450km (280 miles)**

Armament:

Main: **1 x 120mm smoothbore gun**

Secondary: **1 x 12.7mm and 1 x 7.62mm MGs**

AMX Leclerc of the French Army's 3rd Squadron, 503rd RRC, in 1998. Named after the general in command of the Free French 2nd Armoured Division that liberated Paris in 1944.

gunner or commander to select six different targets to be engaged in just over 30 seconds and a new active armour package, the Leclerc looks ready for every eventuality—although it is, as yet, untested in combat. Leclerc is also fitted with the Galix combat vehicle protection system. Eighteen 80mm grenade launch tubes are fitted on the turret to launch smoke or anti-personnel grenades or infrared decoys.

The production figure of 862 includes 66 ARVs and two trainers; other members of the Leclerc family include the EPG armoured engineer vehicle and the DNG battlefield repair tank.

# Type 99

## Main Battle Tank | China | 2001

The Type 99 series (also known as ZTZ-99 and WZ-123), built by Norinco, is the latest and most advanced Chinese MBT, based on the previous Type 98, which in turn was based on the Russian T-72, but which has now undergone so many adaptations as to make it an almost new AFV. Its Russian roots can be seen in its active and passive armour suites, its electro-optical countermeasures (an infrared and laser jamming system) its crew of three and use of an autoloading firing system for its 125mm smoothbore main gun, along with the 9M119 Refleks anti-tank guided missile, all of which are produced in China under a local licence.

However, German influences can be seen its new angular welded turret shape, reminiscent of the Leopard and in its powerpack: a 1,500hp turbocharged liquid-cooled diesel engine, derived from the German MB871. Co-operation with Israel has also led to the

---

### SPECIFICATION

**Variant: Type 99A1**
**Crew: 3**
**Entered service: 1999**
**Weight: 57.000kg (56 tons)**
**Dimensions:**
**Length: 11m (36ft)**
**Height: 2.37m (7ft 10in)**
**Width: 3.5m (11ft 6in)**
**Armour: 100mm (4in) max**

**Engine: Derived from the German MB871ka501, a 12-cylinder diesel developing 1,500hp with a top speed of 80kph (50mph)**
**Range: 600km (373 miles)**
**Armament:**
**Main: 1 x 125mm smoothbore gun**
**Secondary: 1 x 7.62mm coaxial and 1 x Type 85 12.7mm AA**

---

The Chinese Type 99 is the main weapon of the Chinese PLA. Note the 125mm smoothbore which can also fire ATGW and, it is thought, depleted uranium weapons.

development of a Chinese shell based on the Israeli 125mm APFSDS M711 round.

These armour upgrades and a larger turret to fit more equipment and ammunition have seen the vehicle's weight climb to 58 tons. This turret-stored ammunition makes the Type 99 vulnerable to fire once penetrated despite its fire suppression systems and the addition of 20–30mm (0.8–1.2in) of high hardness armour plate over the explosive reactive armour on

either side of the main gun. Its fire control system has been updated with new thermal-imaging observation and targeting systems, a new ballistic computer and dual axis stabilisa-tion that ensures accurate and effective firing whilst on the move.

Due to the high cost of production and consequent small numbers the latest Type 99 is issued only to the most elite armoured divisions of the PLA.

# K2 Black Panther

## Main Battle Tank | S Korea | 2014

The South Korean K2 Black Panther is a fourth-generation MBT designed to replace the K1 and other older AFVs of the ROK, using indigenous technologies and production facilities. The K1 series had been based mainly on the US Abrams but following over a decade of design and development, production of the new South Korean K2 MBT began in 2007.

However, the project has not been without its problems—currently primarily automotive. It had originally been planned to have a Korean engine based on the German MTU890, but domestic versions have been plagued with problems that have consistently held up production and so German engines have been chosen as a temporary solution. The vehicle was also originally designed to have a German main gun—Rheinmetall's experimental 140mm—but following the cancellation of that program the 120mm L55 was chosen instead. It is served by an autoloader (thus keeping crew numbers to three) similar in design to that

### SPECIFICATION

**Crew: 3**
**Entered service: 2014**
**Weight: 54,867kg (54 tons)**
**Dimensions:**
**Length: 10.8m (35ft 5in)**
**Height: 2.4m (7ft 10in)**
**Width: 3.6m (11ft 10in)**
**Armour: Classified**
**Engine: MTU-890 12-cylinder**

**diesel developing 1,500hp with a top speed of 70kph (43mph)**
**Range: 450km (280 miles)**
**Armament:**
**Main: 1 x 120mm Rheinmetall smoothbore gun**
**Secondary: 1 × 7.62mm coaxial and 1 × 12.7mm K6 MGs**